Furnishing the City

Furnishing the City

Harold Lewis Malt

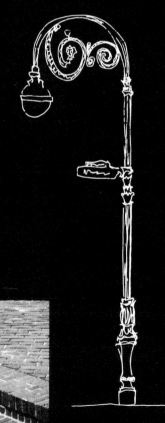

McGraw-Hill Book Company

New York
St. Louis
San Francisco
Dusseldorf
London
Mexico
Panama
Sydney
Toronto

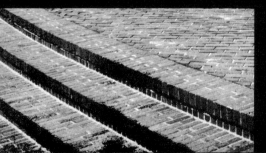

Parking

Sponsoring Editor William G. Salo
Director of Production Stephen J. Boldish
Designer Naomi Auerbach
Editing Supervisor Barbara Church
Editing and Production Staff Gretlyn Blau,
   Carol Ferrari, Teresa F. Leaden, George E. Oechsner

FURNISHING THE CITY

ISBN 07-039845-3

234567890 HDBP 754321

Preface

Industrial designers are concerned with consumer use and acceptance of industrialized processes and products. At Carnegie-Mellon University we students of Kostellow, Lepper, Müller-Munk, were trained as generalists. We made design studies of communications, transportation, and even street furniture—traffic signals, fire hydrants, street lights—all the products that are supposed to make our cities habitable.

Later, at Syracuse with Arthur Pulos, we enlarged our studies to consider user needs in the complete public environment.

Since then much has changed. Standard of living. Technology. Man has gone to the moon while on earth your home is furnished with many amenities, labor-saving, comfort-producing devices such as TV, garbage disposal, automatic furnace or air conditioner. Yet outside, American cities are far uglier than they need be. The American street is still furnished with the same old junk and cities are buying more of the same. How is this possible?

This book looks at the problems and suggests modes of action for those concerned or responsible for renewing the older city and furnishing the new. Although much has been written recently about urban design, the point of view expressed here is not the excessively romantic, worshipful attitude toward nature, shaped and colored by European ideals and training.

The fact is, the streetscape now is synthetic not natural. No longer do grass and trees make the connection between man and his environment. Urban design has become the art of dealing with the artificial. Nine out of ten Americans will soon be contained within a totally manufactured envelope. For better or for worse, streets, sidewalks, traffic signs, mailboxes, light poles, and hundreds of products yet undesigned will make up the urban fabric which must be assembled from the consumer point-of-view. The task is to use technology in a more socially successful way.

While serving as design consultant to aerospace industries and federal agencies, I was exposed to the systems design and management approach. Here was a problem-solving technique proven successful in accommodating large numbers of complex interdependent variables in sophisticated outer-space design. I was anxious to try it on earth-bound environmental design. Fortunately the opportunity came to apply a few of these ideas on campuses being built for the State University Construction Fund of New York. Some of the concepts developed here were first suggested to Dr. Anthony Adinolfi and appeared in *Site Products,* a manual of performance criteria written for the Fund.

But the big need is in the cities and these ideas were shaped in discussions with many people concerned with the quality of the urban environment. Howard Cayton, George Karas, Robert McCabe, Dorn McGrath, Jr., and Ralph Warburton particularly encouraged my attempt to introduce technical innovation.

Theories became reality with a U.S. Department of Housing and Urban Development Demonstration Grant. The city of Cincinnati was enabled to retain me as consultant for the application of the systems approach to the streetscape design of a specific urban renewal project.

For this book, the system becomes the ordering device as well as the content. Part One defines the urban product environment: problems, goals, and systems design approach. Part Two is about the man in the street— the guy who pays the bills and deserves better. Part Three develops performance and evaluation criteria for each component in the manufactured environment.

Like any designer, I have been tempted to do some blue-sky sketching, but this book does not attempt a quantum jump. It really isn't necessary. Nobody has to guess about the year 2000 when exciting, significant, and innovative results can be achieved within the state-of-the-art and the tools available now.

Harold Lewis Malt

Contents

Part One

Systems

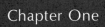

Chapter One

Our Hand-me-down Street Furniture

During a time of increasing population and wealth the American city has deteriorated—decayed and grown dull and deadly. An important but little-recognized force in this ongoing process is the sleazy, shoddy furnishings in the public streets and places.

What are these man-made elements that collectively connect people to the urban visual and functional scene? Do these artifacts have a common heritage? Did their form and manner of use evolve from the needs and technical capabilities of other eras? What was their importance in other times, and how meaningful can these earlier solutions be in contemporary America?

Before setting off to explore new dimensions, let us for a moment look backward from the point of view of the urban designer and the user. Let us mark some of the milestones which may help us determine future goals and evaluate various design approaches.

The Marketplace Marks Downtown

From the very beginning, people came together in a place and by their use made it a public space. They came together for elemental reasons: security, trade, social relationships. The life or death of primitive communities was quickly decided by basic facts: the economic, physical, and emotional needs of their people and how well they were satisfied. And as the people became less nomadic and more stabilized, the settlements evolved into communities with varying patterns of land division, all of which reserved by common agreement certain spaces for public access and use.

Much is made of the geometry of cities and the question of which physical layout may be best. The fact is that over the ages most Old World cities grew by happenstance, and many of these formless organisms endured and became rich in urban imagery. The street became not only a way to go but a place to be.

The more ordered forms of circulation and shelter usually shaped themselves into one of two classic patterns. The more simple is that of the hunter, which is still in use today in Africa, where primitive bush tribes surround the chief's compound with *circles* of huts and cattle pens. The important people are in the center where they want to be. The ring of huts of the others helps keep the livestock in and the enemy out. The soundness of this defensive planning has been thoroughly documented on TV, where regularly the wagon train forms a circle and the encircling redskins are picked off one by one. Serving the social purposes of primitive people most of the year, the central public space was equipped for a more important function. There campfire or religious rites provided the psychological warmth that helped meld the tribe. From the time of Stonehenge this kind of civic "theater-in-the-round" gave meaning to the tribes' existence. Altar benches or braziers were the most significant pieces of public furniture, and their design and use enhanced the tribes' position in a primitive world.

The *grid* pattern, which came later, was developed by the farmer, who plowed and sowed and divided land in a more geometric rectilinear manner. His settlements straggled along linear paths leading to the farming areas.

Regardless of form and almost simultaneously, these agricultural communities grew into populous cities of civilized permanence in many parts of the world. The cities of Mesopotamia, Peru, Mesoamerica, and China are all rich in examples of enriched or monumental urban design. But we start with Europe as the birthplace of Western ideals.

Antiquity is rich in examples of pedestrian malls such as Trajan's Forum, but the democratic way of life found expression in the development of the linear street. In Athens the road from the agora, or marketplace, led not only out to the country but back up to the Acropolis. It became not only a highway but a city street and a sacred way. Here was where the activity was. Stores and shops followed the people; banking and politics were not far behind. Soon came the golden age of Greece, when the rising standard of living created disposable income which the Athenians used to create a magnificent urban setting—spectacular and thrilling yet warm and comfortable. It was a place not only to visit but to live in.

The Athenian citizen, rich or poor, had a variety of places to go and things to enjoy. He could walk around the bottom of the hill, where the modest commercial buildings of the agora were grouped around a large open space near the business and civic center. The facades of these low buildings changed from time to time, as in any modern city, but were always in human scale and related to the square. Sculpture was abundant, the principal form of esthetic expression. It matters not that in retrospect art historians prefer the archaic sculpture to the later Hellenistic period, whose techniques mass-produced perfect torsos. This was an art for the people, and the city dweller could enjoy this urban space lavishly decorated with public art in the Greek humanistic and sensuous style of nude representation.

Nearby and built into the side of the hill was the Council House, where people sat on semicircular stepped seats. Or they went further along the base of the hill to the theater to hear the dramatic works of Sophocles, Euripides, or Aeschylus. And there was the broad flight of steps that led up the slopes of the Acropolis. These provided a clear view of the temple as well as serving as spectator seats for observing agora activities or just girl-watching.

Today the temple complex with Parthenon high on the sacred Acropolis surely is one of the most memorable urban landmarks in all the world. The emotional impact of this clearly defined cityscape must have been even more effective during the ancient ceremonies. Such an occasion was the Panathenaic procession along the Panathenaic Way.

Edmund Bacon tells us that the Panathenaic Way was far more than a city street. It was part of a regional way that linked some of the most sacred places in Greece. By 600 B.C. the road led from mystic graves through a pass to the Dipylon gate of the walled city of Athens and on up the slopes of the Acropolis. It was an important traffic artery used constantly by the people for many purposes. But the street had still another spectacular use.

Once a year a procession went through the city and up the hill to the gold and ivory statue of Athena in the Parthenon. This parade of horses and people was exceptionally stirring because everyone could become involved. Sculptors dramatically recorded its fervor on the Parthenon frieze.

Macy's Thanksgiving Day Parade.

And this event clearly was the organizing force providing the theme for the design and furnishing of this Athenian Main Street, whose every detail was planned to give *pleasure* to the people. The procession was the fore-runner of the American institutionalized parade, whose bands and floats stimulate sales by attracting attention, bringing pedestrian traffic downtown, and contributing imagery and zest to city living.

People Want Public Works

The shape and quality of the public right-of-way has almost always sym-bolized the attitude of the government to the governed. The emotional value of parade streets and public places surely was known to the theocracy governing the cities of the Maya. Although little has been documented, their skill in the planning, programming, and building of vast urban com-plexes is self-evident. Working apart from the mainstream of Western civilization, these priests and nobles created many splendid environments of engineering substance and pleasing imagery.

Without wheel or horse, the Mayan central city was a huge pedestrian mall. The *streetscape* was deliberately designed with many levels and pedestrian concourses to contrast with the surrounding flat plain and achieve a three-dimensional quality. Chichén Itza, founded in A.D. 432 near the Yucatan coast, was such a city.

The designers first defined and walled a huge space 1,600 feet square. Within, the floor was thrust upward and modeled into an exciting mixture of functional forms. The focal point was the lofty Pyramid of Kukulcan. Nearby was the tall cylindrical Caracol—the observatory. A vast rectangular pit lined with stone contained a ball court. Berms and platforms became theatrical stages. And the marketplace was defined by the still-standing Colonnade of a Thousand Columns. Today, walking the steps, ramps, and different levels of Chichén Itza, one achieves a kinesthetic experience of involvement with the environment. In the previous era this sensation was intensified through the staging of many annual events during April and May, when special furnishings, copal incense, and lighting were provided. One event filled with pageantry was the sacrificial rite. Elaborately costumed priests led a muffled-drum procession 900 feet along the ceremonial road to the sacred cenote. Here, from the brink of the huge natural well, a blue-painted maiden was thrown into the green water 80 feet below.

Why human sacrifice? How could the Maya build their magnificent monumental stone structures working without metal and with only stone axes? What motivated the production of so profuse a public art? It all stemmed from corn.

Corn was the preoccupation of the world of the Maya, and Chac-Mool was their benevolent rain god. When it rained, the corn grew, so fast that the farmer labored only forty-eight days to produce his yearly needs. He was grateful to Chac-Mool, and he had nine to ten months leisure time during which he built the city. He would not support an army or warfare, but he did give freely for public facilities. But when there was a long drought, the Maya toppled their idols, abandoned their cities, went into the jungles, and were reduced to eating bark. In this "boom or bust" existence there evolved a public sculpture of harsh esthetic which depicted in bas-relief not only trade and sports but the skull and crossbones and human sacrifice.

Even greater than Chichén Itza was the three-dimensional city of Tikal. The site, a limestone outcropping between two ravines in the rain forest of what is now Guatemala, is spectacular. With visionary planning and immense effort the stone was hewed level, the ravines were made into reservoirs, and public buildings were begun. Soon five groups of buildings covered a square mile. By the middle of the ninth century eight pyramids had been built, four of which were as high as twenty-story buildings. The Great Plaza, at the base of the pyramids, was studded with texture and interest. Although highly ordered and disciplined and containing huge buildings, this plaza seems comfortable and human-scale even today, perhaps

Colonnade of a Thousand Columns, Chichén Itza, Yucatan.

Working without mortar, unskilled labor built the walls of Kabah and Uxmal of interlocked standardized stone shapes.

because of the stepped-back shape of the pyramids, which opens up the space. This ziggurat form invites and challenges climbing. And in the act of climbing the changing elevation constantly creates new perspectives of exciting visual scenes of smaller plazas and pedestrian concourses which were meant to be enjoyed from all views and approaches as a total experience. All this was the Downtown, with a high density of permanent population.

While the Maya had no need for city streets to channel conveyances, they did connect their many cities by sacebob, a road system of ceremonial as well as trading use. Frequently its public roads for runners and litter carriers became causeways elevated above swamps and were paved with crushed limestone packed smooth.

Another important Mayan city, noted for the quality of its urban design and sculpture, was Uxmal. Uxmal was a smaller city built without pyramids; it was not a capital city. Yet its designers evolved a way of building large structures without mortar through the interlocking of standardized, sculptured stones. The mosaic of thousands of these mass-produced stones cast an extravagant pattern of shadow detail that somehow unified the space. The most noted urban structure that achieved this effect was the House of the Governors, sometimes called the single most magnificent building ever erected in the Americas. This palace, 320 feet long, was built on a 5-acre podium 50 feet high. And positioned before the main axis, much like the obelisks with which Renaissance popes marked their plazas, was an enormous stone phallus.

The streetscapes of these Mayan cities, with their varied levels, terraces, and platforms, show the skill of Mayan designers, who, working without the slave manpower or metal of ancient Rome, were still able to model public spaces of intensified imagery. These monumental public works were made possible by a bureaucracy of priests and nobles able to devote a considerable portion of the public wealth to meeting the psychological as well as physiological needs of society.

Public Art Must Be Mass-produced

In medieval times ideas parallel to those of ancient Greece found new expression in Europe. After centuries of transition from castle stronghold to guild and burgher mentality, more humane ideas took hold. While the castle remained aloof, the square and surrounding streets filled with houses and shops of tradesmen and craftsmen. The town became the focus of an agricultural area, and its growth and material success created the need for marketplaces, which became the equivalent of the agora.

But the medieval town remained small, kept within the limits of its ability to defend and support itself. At the peak of the towns' growth in the fourteenth century only Milan and Venice exceeded 100,000 population. Paris, the largest northern town, boasted 80,000 people, while England only had one great town of 40,000 people—London.

All these towns grew without plan or order. Residential streets were added haphazardly, following the terrain up and down. They were narrow, crooked, confusing, and often dead ends. Garbage was dumped from windows; sewage flowed along the rutted lanes. The scale and effect on the senses were personal, human, and immediate.

The commercial street from city gate to marketplace was usually wider, but even here, because of close viewing conditions, the backs of important

"Nunnery" (Government Building), Uxmal, Yucatan circa A.D. 900. An immense Mayan quadrangle whose various steps, levels, setbacks, and wall mosaics create an exciting public space of human scale.

Laundry hanging over narrow pedestrian lanes in old Barcelona still contributes to medieval personal scale.

buildings were ignored and the square was a two-dimensional space. Urban design consisted of making the facades of facing buildings interesting. The accessible front of the church had to develop into a vertical expression to be seen. And as the most dramatic feature of the town, a thirteenth-century Gothic cathedral such as Chartres or the duomo of Florence became not only a house of worship but the town landmark symbol and a work of public art.

How did the power structure of the community accomplish this within the financial resources of the people? How were the services of so many gifted artists secured? Where were they found? Who trained them? If lacking in sophisticated tools and technology, the master builder of a great cathedral had a powerful force going for him—communications. He could meet with the craftsmen and discuss their production problems as part of his conception of new design ideas. Problem solving was cooperative; action was immediate.

Moreover, on closer look we see that most cathedral stones are square standardized blocks. Their shapes are formalized, and they are as repetitively carved as the stones of Mayan Uxmal. They were literally the mass-produced components of a building system and could be assembled with a maximum amount of systematic labor and a minimum of spontaneity.

Although this public art had a technical side involving calculation, the designer and artisan were given the chance to make utilitarian forms into symbolic ones. This came about as medieval society attained new capabilities that led to the growth of powerful political states. Certain towns in these states enjoyed advantages because of strategic location or the favor of a ruler. In the guildhall of the town a spirit developed among the merchants and townspeople that led to the development of a cohesive and powerful bourgeoisie. This class had the organization and drive that evolved the livable community. The guilds spent lavishly on public shows. They encouraged creative work, and shrewdly they were willing to pay for it. The average guildsman was both entrepreneur and artisan. As Giedion pointed out, that extra effort had no technical value—water doesn't drain better out of a gargoyle's mouth than a weep hole in a wall. But the burghers found the contribution of the designer as well as the developer, the sculptor as well as the mason, of public value in adding passion and ecstasy to a city which otherwise offered only toil and existence.

Talent Needs a Patron

Not all towns had benevolent rulers or a cohesive bourgeoisie. Many communities founded in middle Europe in the twelfth or thirteenth century had dogged struggles with feudal lords that laid the foundations for modern

Students celebrating matriculation day at the University of Florence. The fragile beauty of the medieval cathedral is destroyed by the intrusion of the automobile into the pedestrian space.

The "David" of Michelangelo, Florence. Public art of popular appeal.

democracy. By the dawn of the Renaissance the economic center had shifted from town to court. But the city republics of Italy—Venice, Siena, and above all Florence—had achieved an independence of spirit that fostered great public works and public art for the enjoyment of the people.

In the Florence of the early Renaissance everyone was involved in an urban renewal program sponsored by the local governing families, whose money grants gave opportunity to talent and supported innovation. In some cities the stately open squares took hundreds of years to complete. The noblest of them all, the Piazza San Marco in Venice, remained unfinished for five hundred years. But in Florence, Brunelleschi added the dome to the duomo in 1420, Giotto and Pisano shortly afterward added the campanile, and other architects and sculptors quickly contributed buildings, statues, and squares. Many major talents helped plan the town. Leonardo da Vinci, for example, drew designs by means of which the Arno River was straightened as it flowed through Florence. He also proposed a scheme for separation of wheeled from pedestrian traffic by means of different levels. As in any urban renewal or public art project, there was controversy. Michelangelo's heroic statue of David was stoned because of the conspicuous genitalia. But there was interest; there was action.

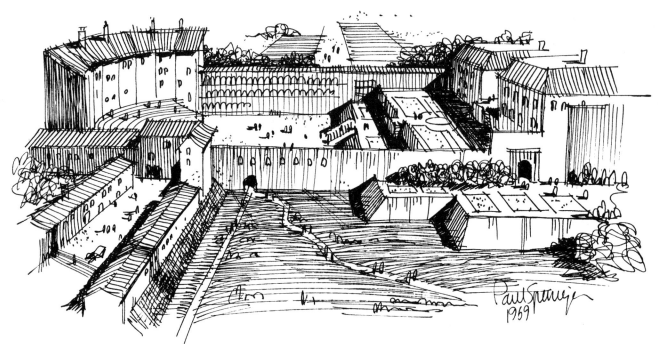

*Multilevel gardens at the Vatican create
new sensory experience for pedestrians.*

Rome, however, was a different place, a city with an indifferent theocracy and a spiritless populace. At the close of the thirteenth century the population had shrunk to 17,000 people crowded into a fold of the Tiber River. The city was a polluted, pestilent place whose dominant visual component was the fortress Castel Sant'Angelo—a place of refuge for the Pope when the Vatican was attacked.

Not until the 1500s, when popes from mercantile families established a business center on the other side of the Ponte Sant'Angelo, was revitalization possible. With the arrival of merchants and bankers—and the reestablishment of the church, newly returned from the sanctuary of the Palais des Papes in Avignon, France—a physical transformation took place.

These new urban popes sponsored many innovative schemes to create order and grandeur from decay and chaos. They accepted large design solutions which flowed from physical needs. One problem was the mixture of blighted buildings and streets left over from many previous epochs plus the terrain, whose Roman hills made large-scale imposition of formal grid layouts impossible. The solution came from designer Donato Bramante, who modeled the three-dimensional floor as a unifying element to the varied streetscape. With levels and turns on different planes, his monumental stairways, terraces, and ramps of the Garden Court of Belvedere at the Vatican became a new element for urban design. The widespread adoption of this technique made Rome a kinesthetic as well as esthetic experience.

Sixtus V was the greatest planner and administrator of the time. Assuming the papacy in 1585 at the age of sixty-four, in the just five years before he died of malaria he planned and executed a public works program that brought urban order to what was still a sprawling, disorderly medieval city. He did it by going out to the neighborhoods. He did not neglect the religious core of Rome; he sponsored the addition of the cupola to St. Peter's dome and placed Caligula's obelisk in the center of the facing plaza. But most importantly Sixtus saw the city in its entirety and knew that public works of social benefit were essential to future growth.

First he changed a random group of roads into an urban transport system. Then he located future squares and plazas and marked them with obelisks. The brilliant use of Egyptian obelisks left over from the Roman days established nodes in the movement system and marked the focal points. Some of the roads and great squares were not completed for decades afterward, but the concept was indisputably established: the sheer presence of these permanent massive landmarks made the land-use decision irreversible.

In the short time Sixtus was Pope Rome rapidly grew, with more shops and houses accommodating an increased population. Then a water supply for the expanding city was urgently needed. His imaginative solution was to restore the old Roman aqueducts, which could conduct water to the highest elevations of the Roman hills, where the system terminated in important microarchitecture and street furniture—twenty-seven fountains in all. Many are in use now. The lion heads of the Moses Fountain still spit water to the passerby. But in Sixtus's time the fountain was also a cluster of street facilities: basins for horses and cattle, a public washing place for dirty laundry, a nearby community bath.

Providing *street furnishings* in public places quickly changed the character of the city, so much so that after some absence a priest returning to Rome wrote that he could hardly recognize the place: "Everything seemed so new—edifices, streets, squares, fountains, aqueducts, obelisks."

Plazas were essential to the needs of the Renaissance cities because they provided an ordered oasis amidst urban squalor. Sixteenth-century designers experimented with all sizes and shapes of plazas in all the major cities of Europe. But there was still one unsolved problem in urban design: tying the whole city together. This technique came from the park designers.

"L'état, c'est moi." The personal life of the monarch became the center of all state activity in the seventeenth century. The rise of the egoistic and ruthless despot began to supersede communal action. Rule changed from a public function to a private gesture. The baroque rulers of Europe such as Louis XIV hated large cities, narrow streets, and common people. Also during this time the feminine influence on court life grew. There was a demand for greater comfort and delicacy. Painting, sculpture, and interior

Der Stadt, Vienna, 1858. Designed for a figure on horseback (Franz Josef I), the Renaissance-inspired plaza has been conquered by the Volkswagen.

furnishings became mannered. The time was ripe for a change in the form and exterior furnishing of the royal residence, and Louis XIV boldly built his new residential and administrative complex in the country instead of in Paris.

Never before had so large a community (court society) been housed under such a roof (2,000 feet long). Started in 1661, the Chateau of Versailles was almost a half century in the making. Deliberately creating an environment for the aggrandizement of the royal ego and the pleasure of the court, the park designer, André Lenôtre, produced a palace that dominated the town behind it and nature before it. The doing required the development of a total landscape system of geometric design which, like later town planning, related a great number of components in a carefully ordered natural environment.

Versailles was conceived as a setting for the pedestrian activity of court society. It was also to be a royal extravaganza. Lenôtre therefore furnished the landscape with every imaginable feature, including lakes and a grand canal with gondolas; adult and children playgrounds; terraces, pools, and fountains; a zoo; and formal gardens. New standards of elegance were achieved for public furniture such as pavings, benches, balustrades, and lanterns. But the outstanding innovation was in the ordering device for so many parts. Lenôtre used a radial design that organized town and parks like spokes about the hub of the palace and aligned principal axes with main landscape features. The central and most important viewing axis was the highway from Paris, which led straight into the royal stables, penetrated the thin, long palace, and continued with clean vista over foreground gardens to the distant horizon. This system for ordering a complex of monumental buildings and vast parks produced so majestically simple a visual scene that it was reproduced in Vienna for the Austrian royal palace Schönbrunn and similarly adapted and applied around the world.

HANDMADE TO MACHINE-MADE

Engineering the Environment

The eighteenth century was a time of change, and the industrial revolution altered the appearance of cities far more than the social revolution. It was time for product innovation, and the urge to invent swept England in the 1760s like a national fever. Investors put money into new gadgets, schemes, products, and processes conceived by hundreds of unlikely persons. Farmers and a new breed of entrepreneurs contributed ideas as well as craftsmen. This excitement and acceleration in product development was given weight and substance by radical improvement in an old process—the making of iron.

Iron was hated and distrusted by classical architects, with much reason: although there had been ironworks since the fourteenth century and skilled armorers had forged the metal into useful and handsome lanterns, grilles, and railings, iron was expensive to work. Outdoor use in towns demonstrated other deficiencies, such as poor resistance to corrosion. But new qualities were given to the old metal by a succession of refinements. Abraham Darby invented the mechanical process of wet-sand casting in 1708. Now unskilled labor could make molten metal flow over the artisan's pattern and repetitively reproduce intricate designs at low cost. Other ideas quickly came from Darby and others. By the middle of the century the blast furnace was improved, making possible higher heats, improved metallurgy, and a new product—structural iron.

Many building tasks formerly reserved for stone could now be performed better by cast or wrought-iron beams and posts. Large lacy-looking bridges, aviaries, pavilions, and previously unheard-of structures were soon engineered to make daring use of this new exotic material. On Main Street, building technique and facade appearance were completely transformed within one hundred years. The framing of great halls with open ironwork, supported on thin cast columns and enclosed with glass, was quickly accepted. In the same period, because of this bounty of new mechanical products and processes to show and sell, the regional fair exploded into the international exhibition. And what more fitting a promotional technique than to house new factory-made iron-age products in an iron prefabricated structure? So the London 1851 International Exhibition of Machines was held in a Crystal Palace more dreamlike than any Renaissance palace. Joseph Paxton's systems design of small, serially repeated shop-made units was as dramatic in impact and import as Buckminster Fuller's geodesic dome of steel and acrylic units of Expo 67. The massive, traditional, Renaissance stone structure had disappeared, and in its place was a light tracery against the sky.

The machine esthetic was here, as the people realized if the academy did not. When the Parisian public protested about the unsuitability of a new group of market buildings made of stone, Baron Georges Eugène Haussmann, prefect of Paris under Louis Napoleon, made the architect tear them down and turn to iron and glass. Now this concept was expanded and revitalized, in Les Halles Centrales, the meat, fruit, and vegetable market of Paris, begun in 1853. It was a vast covered marketplace with a high transparent ceiling—so huge a place that it contained groups of pavilions, cobbled streets, and streetlamps on columns. Its utilitarian structures, stark and simple, with lacy iron vaults overhead that optically disappeared in the pouring sunlight, created a new esthetic feeling. "It looked like some great outsize modern machine, a great boiler for a people's digestion, a gigantic metal stomach

Crystal Palace, London, 1851.

with iron, glass and wood, riveted, bolted together, so elegant, so powerful. . . ." Such was Émile Zola's description of Les Halles.

These mechanical-looking marvels had such fascination for people that,
like today's huge domed sports stadium, they established another function:
landmark. In some instances this function became preeminent. The Eiffel
Tower is one example. What an exuberant gesture, this 1,000-foot structure
with no function except to afford people the pleasure of ascending and

enjoying the view! The lesson of the emotional content achievable through the penetration of space by means of daring engineering sparked fanciful constructions such as the huge ferris wheel in the Prater, visible over much of Vienna, and continues to modern times with Saarinen's stainless-steel arch of St. Louis.

By definition these landmarks were novelties and unique. But businessmen and developers quickly grasped the central point. Iron was economical. Its use eliminated thick load-bearing walls and permitted longer spans with fewer supports, which meant more net usable space. Iron structures could be prefabricated in a factory and more quickly assembled on site. Businessmen recognized that the resultant imagery was valuable, but it was a byproduct, a bonus.

The interest of the business community provided the incentive for further experimentation. New techniques were developed for the factory manufacture of precisely dimensioned parts whose rivet holes would align during field assembly. New York took the highroad in 1868 with the erection of the first elevated railroad, the West Side and Yonkers Patented Railroad. While back in Paris, bridge designer Gustave Eiffel in 1876, thirteen years before his famous tower, built the Bon Marché department store and proved the commercial feasibility of iron and glass.

The use of natural light and air as a design element made possible a new shopping environment. The pleasurable atmosphere changed the design not only of the individual store but of the business street itself. The street frequently became an arcaded open space, as in Milan with the Galleria Vittorio Emanuele or as in Naples with the Galleria Umberto—both still in use. In America arcades were built in most major cities. The Cleveland Arcade—a complex of two nine-story office buildings linked by a central skylighted mall surrounded by four stories of shops and offices—is still functioning. These galleries were patronized by elegant society and became instant commercial successes. Their social as well as commercial values became the prototype for the contemporary regional covered shopping center, whose entertainment value as an all-day experience may be as important to the shopper as the location, convenience, and mass display of goods.

The Prater, Vienna.

Furnishing the Environment

Until the industrial revolution, street furniture in most cities consisted of the lantern, hitching post, and occasional bench. When used, street identification consisted of handmade plaques frequently of great artistry appliquéd to the walls of buildings at street intersections.

Lighting was a spotty practice, and oil-burning lanterns required the lamplighter to tend the wick. The flickering dim light was almost always cast too close to the supporting building. Only rarely did a handsome wrought-iron bracket cantilever the lantern far enough out over the street.

Then came the gas lamp, whose greenish yellow light brightened the nighttime scene of the nineteenth-century city. Frederick Albert Winsor patented his process for manufacturing gas from coal and staged the first public street lighting in 1807 along Pall Mall in London. But acceptance did not come easily in Europe; progress was delayed by prejudice and fear. Tastemakers such as Sir Walter Scott in England and Napoleon in France scoffed at the idea of lighting cities with smoke. While it was possible to install new utilities below ground, out of sight and mind, above ground these new engineered products were disparaged and resisted by academicians trained in the static viewpoint of the Renaissance. So that in Europe the appearance of street furniture and the visual scene remained unchanged for some time. In America, however, gas-lamp street lighting was gaining accept-ance as early as 1815, when Baltimore became the first city to light most of its streets with gas, manufactured by a company founded by Rembrandt Peale.

The invention of the cast-iron hollow column eliminated all remaining resistance to street lighting. Although it was invented for other structural purposes, the advantages for street lighting of this English product of about 1790 were readily apparent. Now light could be evenly distributed in a linear pattern from lanterns put where needed and independent of building facades for support. This new kind of street furniture also could be put to other use. So while England and the Continent continued the custom of placing street names on building facades, in America, where developers were build-ing streets before houses existed, street signs appeared on lampposts. Addi-tional signs have been added since, until the support has become more signpost than lamppost in function.

While new in concept, these mass-produced components followed traditional styles in appearance. Street furniture became period pieces to complement city architecture. Burgeoning cities in America sought "instant tradition" and bought large monumental light columns in elaborate historical dress for Downtown. And a variety of revivals took place in cast-iron col-umns: Grecian, Gothic (bishop's crook of New York), all the classical styles.

Mechanical to Electrical

In the waning years of the nineteenth century the world was on the threshold of much that was new. Freud was exploring unconscious impulses, the impressionist Monet was painting shifting light, and new "things" were being invented that were energized. Edison turned on the world when he switched from gas flame to electric lamp.

Boston, Massachusetts.

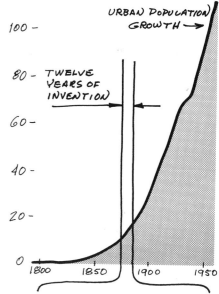

San Francisco, California.

URBAN POPULATION GROWTH →

TWELVE YEARS OF INVENTION

Inventions that shaped the cities.

The generation of electric power at a building site for lighting was quickly adopted and became common by the turn of the century; many new buildings produced their own direct current. Perhaps more important than his carbon glow lamp of 1879 was Edison's development in 1882 of the central electric power station and distribution system. Alternating current facilitated long-distance distribution of power with low power loss. Now brighter illumination of urban America was possible, and new utility lines were soon laid along streets to convert existing gas systems and hardware to electricity.

Power that made lamps hot and glowing could also energize the many new devices required to meet urban needs. Large-scale immigration turned towns quickly into cities which needed more communications. In 1884 telephone wires were strung from New York to Boston.

Simultaneously, in Madrid, Don Arturo Soria y Mata created not only a telephone system but also the first electric streetcar system. Suddenly the trolley ceased to be horse-drawn. Power could move more people about faster and more economically. Speculators and investors saw other opportunities and created many new utilities. Jungles of wire were added to

1877 TELEPHONE Alexander Graham Bell speaks from Salem to his assistant in Boston, 12 miles away.

1880 SKYSCRAPER William LeBaron Jenney builds the first skyscraper, ten stories tall, for the Home Insurance Co. in Chicago.

1880 INCANDESCENT LAMP The first filaments, made of carbonized sewing threads, burn for 40 hours in Edison's laboratory!

1885 ELECTRONIC TROLLEY CAR Baltimore replaces the horse—the first American city to do so.

1886 SUBWAY London is the first city to transport people underground, in an electric-powered system designed by Greathead.

1889 AUTOMOBILE The Daimler is whizzing along the roads at eleven mph!

1889 ELEVATOR Otis brothers install first electric elevator in Demarest building in New York.

Main Street, Buffalo, New York, 1888. A boomtown and place of hullabaloo. Its affluence could be measured by the number of telephone wires draped from poles. Pedestrians were afforded the luxury of crosswalks set in the cobbled streets.

Main Street, Buffalo, New York, 1897. Affluence encourages more sophisticated standards. All utility wires are underground, new electric streetlights installed, the street repaved.

existing wire systems. Poles were planted thicker and higher. Soon the look of the American streetscape was established.

Engineers and draftsmen copied the architectural styles of the past to cloak and provide acceptance to their new inventions. Fire hydrants were fluted like Grecian columns, and fire-alarm mechanisms were housed in cast-iron Cape Cod cottages. In the mechanical age, pre-1900, it was quite easy and proper to use familiar imagery in coping with the new mechanical technology and use it as the design vocabulary for the townscape. That is why cast-iron hydrants and ornate gas lamps look right in early photographs of the city. On the other hand, just as the horseless carriage was the product of buggy manufacturers, so was the traffic signal made by railroad-equipment manufacturers; and although their engineers achieved high reliability standards, the ponderous traffic-control equipment imposed standards of weight and mass more suited to a product squatting beside a train track than suspended in space or pinned to a pole along the street.

MAKING THE CITY GREEN

Beauty and the Bureaucracy

The technical age had dawned, and in Europe Baron Haussmann understood the city as a technical problem. Louis XIV spent a lifetime building Versailles, with all the resources of France at his disposal. Starting in 1853, in just seventeen years Haussmann, as city administrator for Louis Napoleon, transformed Paris at a cost of 2.5 billion francs in the greatest public works programs of all time.

Haussman had to face all the problems of urban renewal, especially the social and political. He saw overall problems of traffic, transportation, and communications, and rather than merely enlarge existing streets, he quickly cut a new street system connecting railroad stations and key points by means of axial boulevards providing exciting vistas. Blocks of buildings were torn down in order to expedite his solutions to long-range problems. But in buying private property for public good, Haussmann made enemies. While some of the corrupt bourgeosie made profits, others called him a ruthless autocrat. And he was forced to leave before implementing his concept of a wide greenbelt around the city utilizing the old girdle of fortifications.

But Haussmann's unique administrative procedures and people remained at work. He had turned from artists and put together a staff of technicians to accommodate the city to the industrial changes involved in the design, installation, and maintenance of public works. For the first time anywhere administrative responsibilities were organized within three departments: water and sanitation, streets and parks, and planning.

Put in charge were engineering graduates of the École Polytechnique. Belgrand constructed the enormous sewer system of Paris and the aqueducts which for the first time provided an adequate water supply. Haussmann put Jean Alphand, a highway engineer, in charge of all landscape work. It was he who laid out the Champs-Élysées and the leisure grounds of Paris, including the kidney-shaped systems of walks used in the parks such as the Bois de Boulogne. He also invented tree-lifting machines that could transplant thirty-year-old trees in full leaf. But most importantly, Deschamps, head of the new municipal planning service, plotted the new street lines that contributed to the unique look of Paris. His boulevards were not only high-speed traffic lanes to the suburbs but also strolling areas for the common man where before had been only packed tenements.

The American Park Movement

More than sixty years before Haussmann started to transform Paris, the Versailles design concept of the grand geometric plan had been adapted by Charles L'Enfant to Washington, D.C. But the impressive boulevards of Paris were highly regarded and copied in most of Europe's capital cities, whereas in America most cities rapidly grew in size and industrial ugliness without relief of boulevard, open space, or greenery (until Frederick Law Olmsted was supported by visionaries).

Olmsted, a well-known social reformer, was also a farmer concerned about improper use of land. He saw the effect of rising urban population on ill-prepared cities and knew it was damaging to democracy. Fortunately, at the same time a few New York City businessmen had a vision of the future needs and growth of their city and in 1856 sponsored a competition to design a city park uptown, forty blocks from where the action was.

Olmsted won the Central Park competition and quickly implemented the self-evident beauty of his park plans and landscape designs there and in many other cities throughout the United States. His designs featured the urban park as an essential part of the city's fabric. Although he learned much from the English park system, Olmsted's contribution was unique. He established the notion that greenery for relaxation with nature must be made available for all.

City-beautiful Era

Around the turn of the century the American economy was booming, waves of immigration were doubling population, America was becoming a world power, and still-young cities were expanding and new ones being born. And until the Great Depression of the thirties, the nation experienced almost continuous urban growth.

Seeking symbols of newfound wealth and status, cities turned away from the machine and returned to classicism. Lacking an acceptable native image, the new cities copied the proved art of ancient Rome and lavished it upon monumental civic centers. As early as 1893, while Europe was still experimenting with the great iron landmarks housing the machine exhibitions, the World's Columbian Exposition at Chicago went back to the Renaissance for inspiration. But in its new adaptation at Chicago and elsewhere, the Renaissance style tended to become a wedding-cake style.

First mechanical traffic signal, illuminated at night with colored lantern, London, 1868.

POLICE NOTICE.

STREET CROSSING SIGNALS.
BRIDGE STREET, NEW PALACE YARD.

CAUTION.	STOP.

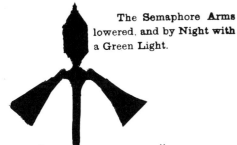

The Semaphore Arms lowered, and by Night with a Green Light.

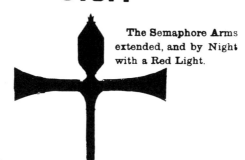

The Semaphore Arms extended, and by Night with a Red Light.

By the Signal "CAUTION," all persons in charge of Vehicles and Horses are warned to pass over the Crossing with care, and due regard to the safety of Foot Passengers.

The Signal "STOP," will only be displayed when it is necessary that Vehicles and Horses shall be actually stopped on each side of the Crossing, to allow the passage of Persons on Foot; notice being thus given to all persons in charge of Vehicles and Horses to stop clear of the Crossing.

RICHARD MAYNE,
Commissioner of Police of the Metropolis

December 10th 1868.

Louis Sullivan predicted that "the damage wrought to this country by the Chicago World's Fair will last half a century"; and true enough, the impact of this wedding-cake style struck the entire country. The Pan American Exposition of 1901 in Buffalo echoed the Chicago pattern of plaster palazzos on a grand canal filled with gondolas. Soon smaller towns emulated these examples and built vulgarized gates, arches, and fountains and even disguised water tanks as battlements or temples of love.

In the years that followed a few planners, such as Daniel Burnham, worked at developing the city in its entirety as a balanced system of parks and streets. Burnham considered the city in terms of essential relationships of systems of circulation arteries, parks, and public spaces. His followers established the urban planning profession and helped develop tools and techniques for control of the environment, such as zoning ordinances.

But in the main this was a period when there was more concern with the external shape of the city—buildings, esplanades, elegant neighborhoods. Few understood or examined the growing environmental problems of Downtown, the slums, and the growing use of motor cars.

The City as a Machine

Meanwhile a few urban designers were fascinated with the potential of practical inventions for solving functional problems. For example, just before the turn of the century Soria y Mata proposed "Linear City" in which utility lines would become the linear basis for city layout, so that houses and buildings could be plugged into water, communications, and power networks. He actually built such a linear city near Madrid, and the Russians used a similar concept in the building of Stalingrad.

France, with such illustrious examples as the Gallerie des Machines, Les Halles, and the Eiffel Tower, produced several visionaries who saw that the machine esthetic could be applied not only to shelter but to the complete environment. Eugène Hénard, architect for the city of Paris between 1900 and 1914, was such a man. His seminal ideas, reported in his book *Les Villes de l'Avenir,* were influential in shaping the directions of others, such as Le Corbusier and Antonio Sant'Elia.

Hénard had many startling ideas. Even before the Wright brothers came to France, he saw the need for an airport available to the city. In 1904, thinking in the then familiar terms of the dirigible, he proposed the first in-city landing field anywhere in the world. He envisioned an airdrome at the Champ de Mars in which the Eiffel Tower would be used as a signal tower and the Gallerie des Machines would become the hangar. As early as 1910 Hénard, clearly seeing that the rising demand for municipal services was creating a jungle of products, recommended the use of *multilevel* streets

Temple of Music, Pan American Exposition, 1901.

in high-density parts of the city. The historian Peter Wolf has reported on Hénard's comments to the Town Planning Conference in London that year. Hénard said that the ordinary street was still a country lane bordered with footpaths, but whose subsurface was layered with sewers and telegraph, electric, and telephone wires all without order or system. "When repair is necessary," Hénard said, "each system, whether it belongs to a private company or to one of the city departments, has to be dealt with separately." And he demonstrated how these services could be integrated. One of his proposals used various levels to accommodate mechanical functions, including ash and garbage collection, and featured vertical circulation to rooftop helicopter pads. All in 1910!

But in America there was little interest in such ideas. Periodically proposals were made for the "city of the future," featuring elevated transporta-

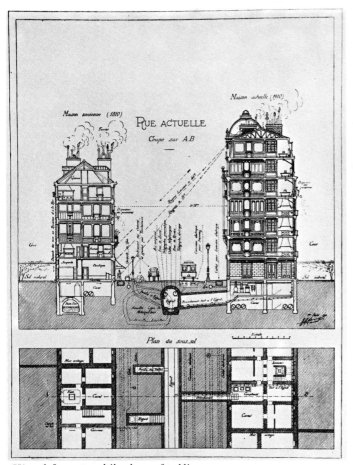

Hénard forecast multilevel use of public space by means of improved technology.

tion schemes in which vehicles ran over rooftops of continuous buildings or, sometimes, over lattice or grid. These variations of "motopia" usually appeared too mechanistic, offered little technological advancement, and received no public support. Most planning emphasis through the twenties and thirties was based on community social values to be achieved by greenbelts and nature rather than mass production and industry. With the passing of the Great Depression, New Deal interest in, and public support of, social change and massive public works waned, and the much-heralded change from bombs to building systems by sophisticated armament industries never developed after World War II.

Meanwhile the population of the country had multiplied from approximately 20 million at the turn of the century to 200 million, and was still soaring. The number of cars on the road had jumped from zero to 90 million and was straining toward double that by the end of the century. A tidal wave of people and products was sweeping over the green land, making it barren and ugly.

Crow's nest, adapted from railroad signal tower, installed on Woodward Avenue, Detroit, circa 1915.

More elegant crow's nest installed on Fifth Avenue New York. Motorists now watch signals rather than policeman inside.

Chapter Two

The Problem

The city has become a jungle of posts and products. Weedlike these dense growths sprout from barren asphalt and concrete and flourish without systematic planting, cultivation, or pruning. The public right-of-way has become encumbered by the thicket of products from building line to center of the street. Community appearance lacks visual as well as functional order.

Not only does the imagery of Downtown suffer; the very quality of the living experience in the neighborhoods or even suburbs is affected. The need to improve the quality and utility of the public environment is important to all. But the greatest difficulty we face in environmental design is the lack of understanding—agreement as to what the actual problems are and what can be done about them.

In order to develop an approach to problem solving, we must first determine what went wrong.

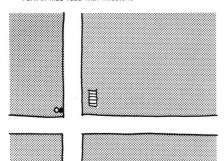

Fork in mud road with milestone

Paved street with gas lamp, street name,
and horse trough

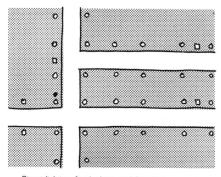

Street lighting, fire hydrant, and fire alarm

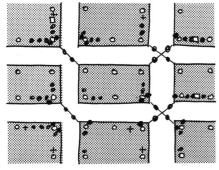

High density products with low-order control

THE HIGH COST OF VISUAL POLLUTION

Product Proliferation

Like a science-fiction story the American love affair with the automobile spawns increasing litters of cars, until the machines displace people from streets and houses, and concrete, not grass, covers the cityscape. The time is rapidly coming when the use of the private automobile on the public street will be curtailed. Cars will be subject to curfew, and their use will be prohibited in some areas. The advantage of the motor vehicle will have been lost through its very abundance. Already, according to testimony before the Senate Roads Subcommittee, the average speed of motor vehicles through the streets of New York has been reduced, in 1966, to 8.5 miles per hour, as compared with 11.5 miles per hour of horse-drawn vehicles in 1907.

This problem is not unique to larger cities or even to America. Europe, whose Renaissance cities are so appealing to American tourists, offers no design guidelines for the automobile age. In fact the elegant plazas and charming side streets of European cities are snarled almost beyond hope. In a typical day, according to London's first traffic commissioner, Peter Scott, "500,000 cars, 8,000 buses and 6,000 taxis jam the streets with the pace reduced to 2 mph during the peak period in, say, Old Kent Road."

While traffic congestion is acknowledged as a problem and highway design forms the basis for many urban studies, another dimension must be added: the number of public products required to sustain and control the private automobile. As will be discussed in a later chapter, the high cost of visual pollution is significant in psychological as well as economic terms; traffic-control devices are masters of people as well as public spaces.

A visual survey of any urban street reveals the extent to which many different products are repetitively required for communication with, and control of, the pedestrian and motorist. And great numbers of other devices are required for lighting, security, and amenity. Up to this time no American city has ever compiled and made available a complete inventory of its street furniture, equipments, and appliances. But some indication of the economic and visual importance of these items can be seen from a 1967 study made for the city of Cincinnati, with a population of 500,000. In just the downtown area of approximately seventy city blocks were contained:

50,000	linear feet roadway paving
90,000	linear feet sidewalk paving
14,000	linear feet crosswalk paving
300	pedestrian signals
250	traffic signals
70	emergency vehicle signals
1,000	traffic-regulation signs

2,000   parking-regulation signs
  935   light fixtures

There were other uncounted publicly owned furnishings, such as mail-boxes, trash receptacles, benches, clocks, phone booths, fire hydrants, signal controllers and detectors, police call boxes, fire-alarm boxes, gratings, parking meters, and landscaping. Peter Kory of the Urban Development Agency of Cincinnati initiated one of the first street-furniture analysis and design programs. But for most other cities the magnitude of the problem remains unrecognized.

And more is yet to come. Lacking study or design programs, the cities will have, as Patrick Geddes put it, "more and more of worse and worse." The size of the public investment in street furniture will increase in response to several forces at work. First, there is the demand spurred by population growth; second, the political and social need to rebuild much of our cities by the end of the century; third, the affluence to support the effort as expressed by voter approval of increased expenditures in the public works segment of national, state, and local budgets. School bond issues are sometimes defeated at the polls, but public works line-items are seldom questioned. However, as the investment in public environment increases, the quality will decrease unless solutions are found to such problems as street-furniture *styling*.

In architecture the monuments are single monuments; in urban design the furnishings are in multiples. A city can be and has been built around a Parthenon. What would be the effect of a thousand Parthenons scattered about the city? A city has light poles and fire hydrants. What is the effect of a thousand monumental light poles or Grecian fire hydrants on the observer? Does this styling approach contribute to an object's efficiency? Presently, most products on the public right-of-way are highly specialized, and each one is allowed to perform only one function. This single-function product-oriented design approach inevitably makes for vast overlapping and duplication of materials and costs. These inefficiencies must be paid for one way or another. If the city and its population were static, it might be possible to reduce the clutter and inefficiency by redesigning individual items. But in a dynamic situation there is urgent need for systematic review of all furnishings.

The real problem is not density of products per se; significantly it is *the way in which density is organized*. But urban areas that require a high order of product density unfortunately have a low order of management control.

Fragmented Bureaucracy

Visualize the result if the average American home were furnished in the following manner: each appliance, lamp, floor covering, article of furniture,

Products fill the public space and leave little room for people.

Erratic, overlapping jurisdictions.

Buffalo, New York. Columbus on his pedestal discovers America to be a forest of poles.

garbage can, picture, telephone, and so on, was selected and purchased by a different member of the family without regard for the needs of others, installed by a different person without regard for whatever already existed nearby, and maintained by still someone else without regard for other housekeeping needs. This approximates the procedure employed by municipal departments in many communities. *Uncoordinated procurement, installation, and maintenance is the rule.*

"The fact is," Lawrence Halprin wrote, "that attention to the detail and design of objects in its streets is as important to the qualities of a city's aesthetics as its buildings themselves—the modern city is a kaleidoscope of overlapping activities and people in motion. As the people eddy and move in a multifaceted series of actions, the furniture in the street becomes the fixed point which can guide and enrich their movements."

This is the need, but what is the reality? Referring to one item, parking meters, the *Buffalo Courier-Express* (Buffalo, New York, population 500,000) editorially complained, "The Board of Parking has no jurisdiction over them, but the Board of Safety decides where they should go; the Common Council decides what kind to buy; the Purchase Division buys them; the Police

Department installs and maintains them; and the Treasury Department collects the money."

With this kind of fragmented authority the ablest urban renewal or public works administration has difficulty in programming and getting a more efficient or esthetically satisfactory environment.

Design innovation is further hampered by the lack of research or test facilities to service the various departmental needs. A bureaucracy of fragmented technical departments lacks corporate muscle in competing for available funds. America is considered an affluent society. Yet when more than 60 percent of most municipal budgets is channeled to education, little is left for other activities such as maintaining the environment. Consequently the planning research of local government is often limited to traffic and land-use studies. Unless there is professional staff manpower or consultants are employed, reliance is placed on suppliers for the preparation of purchase specifications for street furnishings. This common practice leads to quantity rather than quality solutions—wider streets, more traffic signals, bigger signs—more "things," as industrial designer Arthur Pulos calls them.

Then too, codes and manuals of state or federal agencies frequently freeze the furnishings design of the city. Specification-type codes hamper innovation and protect obsolete practices and products. Only partially serving the purpose of protecting the public, regulatory codes do not in themselves create order. Established by yesterday's reform, they are today's fences against progress. However, if existing codes and other forms of minimum design requirements are to be set aside, what will be used for design guidelines? Performance criteria based on *user* requirements. More and more, federal and state aid, which considerably supplements local resources, is used as the leverage to secure the inclusion of generalized design objectives and performance criteria into renewal, housing, and public works programs. A document including these, once approved by funding agencies and the governing body, such as a city council, can become a legal ordinance. The program manager can then use this instrument to supersede narrow-focus codes and to secure the cooperation of all city departments.

Now consider the problem of the bureaucrat faced with the need to procure beauty. By whose standards is beauty defined? How much public money is she worth? How do you describe esthetics in a purchase requisition? *Quality* of environment does not enter into the cost/benefit formula which is the basis for evaluation and selection among public works projects competing for public money. Quality of environment is immediately disadvantaged vis-à-vis more quantifiable factors. It is essential, therefore, that a new design approach be employed which by the nature of its process produces a total environment of quality.

There has already been encouraging experimentation in some centralized

The result of product-oriented specification-type codes and regulations.

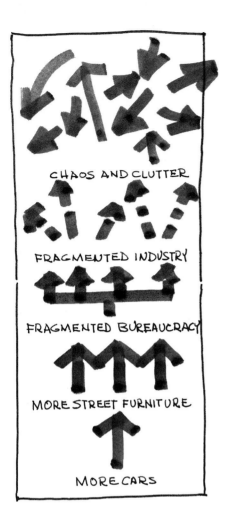

CHAOS AND CLUTTER

FRAGMENTED INDUSTRY

FRAGMENTED BUREAUCRACY

MORE STREET FURNITURE

MORE CARS

(Above, right) *Pollution of the public environment.* (Right) *San Francisco signal replacement. Is the new better than the old?*

administrative situations. Supported by strong mayors, the City Planning Commission of Philadelphia has been able to introduce *élan* into parts of Philadelphia. Planning departments of Minneapolis, Baltimore, and New Haven and a few other cities have received enough support from strong leadership to permit the coordinated process to work. Where the private developer is design-oriented, as the James Rouse organization is, a Columbia (Maryland) can result. Where a public authority directs its planners and designers to produce a complete environment (including parking, graphics, and lighting), a Toronto Airport, a Montreal Metro, or a Fresno Mall can result. When a state recognizes the limitations of splintered public works procedures and creates and finances a separate action organization (State University Construction Fund of New York), then dozens of large complexes of unique environmental character can be built in a few years (the campuses built for the fund). However, the magnitude of the problem is such and these solutions are so few that they project as oases in the urban desert of America.

Municipal mystique blocks consumer feedback and marketplace rejection of absurdity.

Fragmented Industry

Consider a suit of clothes in which the pants were made by one firm, the jacket by another, and the vest by a third—all without reference to each other. In what field of manufacturing and merchandising would such a bizarre practice be tolerated? In street furniture!

Nowhere in America is there available an interrelated line of municipal equipments for furnishing the city. No manufacturer produces more than a narrow segment of the broad spectrum of municipal, campus, airport, or shopping-center needs. Few manufacturers produce all important parts of their own product line. And it is notorious that the component elements comprising a common streetlight—the post, lamp, refractor, and luminaire, for example—are all made by different manufacturers and never meet until married on the sidewalk by the city fathers.

Perhaps these marriages of necessity will work better when the mating is arranged by computer. But this is not likely, and there remains as little contribution to the public good or the enrichment of the environment as there is commonality between equipments.

Why does this condition persist? Because almost all street furniture is still handmade by small nonintegrated producers with older plant and without sophisticated engineering or tooling. Because these handcraft products are installed by conventional construction-trade techniques with reliance on manual labor. Because the fragmentation of the municipal purchasing procedure prevents mass production of a complete environmental "package" and thereby results in higher unitized costs to the public.

Why, more than one hundred years after the industrial revolution, is industry still not convinced of the need to turn to mass production for high-volume distribution of better urban furnishings? Prevailing practice had its roots at the turn of the century, when many small companies began to supply the burgeoning cities' needs. Expertise was not a significant factor in producing nontechnological products; tooling and investment required was nominal; the use of heavy materials such as cast iron in lampposts and fire hydrants favored regional producers.

Now these same producers of street equipment—who were quick to adapt from the mechanical to the electrical age—are slow to advance into electronics. Research money has not been spent for more compact, less obtrusive, better-engineered and -appearing products of improved technology. Consequently industry has not offered products that offset the gap between construction-labor annual productivity and cost increase. The producers' present position remains archaic in a world rapidly moving toward a more rational use of its resources—in the construction industries toward modular control and preferred dimensions, international standards and *industrialized* systems.

THERE OUGHTA BE A LAW!   By Harry Shorten

As yet, few catalog selections of more compact, less obtrusive, and better-engineered products of improved technology can be made. Therefore the city must presently opt to design its own furnishings if it does not wish to add additional inefficient handcrafted articles to those already in the townscape. Some more sophisticated city agencies have sponsored new product designs of greater utility and development. The East Bay Water Works of Sacramento has its own proprietary fire hydrant; the New York Bureau of Gas, Water and Electricity sponsored a unique light standard; the urban renewal and redevelopment agencies of various cities, such as New Haven and Cincinnati, have sought more esthetic furnishings to unify their urban spaces. The number of cities recognizing the need to coordinate the design and siting of furnishings grows as professional planners and others seek to attack the total problem. Their interest will attract enterprises of more sophisticated management into the manufacture and distribution of the necessary environmental components.

Missing link (feedback).

Fragmented Consumer

Lack of feedback from consumer to manufacturer contributes to the perpetuation of inadequate street furniture on the public right-of-way. The manufacturer has contact with only the middleman (bureaucracy). The consumer, literally the man in the street, never sees a variety of shelf goods for comparison shopping. He cannot exercise the traditional veto of the marketplace.

Does not the motorist notice that eleven traffic signals instead of one at an intersection are confusing and dangerous? Of course! Does not a householder know that a glaring bright mercury streetlamp shining in his bedroom window is disturbing and destructive to neighborhood residential values? Of course! Does not the bus rider waiting in the rain without protection question the lack of shelter? Of course! Is not this public passivity in the face of environmental stupidity symptomatic of the emperor's-clothes syndrome, in which no one wants to be first to acknowledge the situation's absurdity? Perhaps. Or it may be that the consumer has not seen any other ways. He may be the victim of *municipal mystique*. He may assume there are no ways to make his environment look better and to provide him with more safety, amenity, and comfort.

We start with names for certain problems—"fire hydrant," "traffic light," "street sign." These names have already done our designing before we start. Because of municipal mystique the public is accustomed to think about these objects as fixed and static *things* rather than look for *solutions to needs* which can take new and different forms at different times depending on local conditions. Therefore people have not questioned the quality and

utility of their public furniture. And street clutter and ugliness have not been improved because there has not been the political need to acknowledge that the public street belongs to the people and is not the bailiwick of highway or other departments to use as they will. Conscientious planners and administrators have had little incentive to disrupt existing practice and face the rigors of innovation. Approving pats on the back come hard-earned for even low-level efforts such as removal of nonproductive or obsolete equipment from the streets.

This condition is in transition. Now the consumer is becoming more attuned to the confusion and ugliness of the environment through the public-opinion-molding mass media—TV documentaries, press editorials and reporting, cartoons and comic strips. The consumer has begun to realize that it is his money that is being spent for public improvements. Soon he will learn to articulate his needs. The city dweller will force purchasing changes by demonstration of his voting power.

Welcome! (Opposite, above) *Brocton, New York.* (Opposite below) *Castroville, California.* (Left) *Town of Amherst, New York.*

Chinatown, San Francisco.

CREATING COMMUNITY IDENTITY
Imagery

"What place is this?"

A quick visual survey of almost every community discloses not only chaos and clutter but also an enormous sameness, a tedious dullness that deadens the civic senses and *joie de vivre*. And this condition will worsen. As towns become cities and cities merge into 600-mile-long megalopolises, local community imagery will become more essential in order to provide a sense of place that the city dweller can cling to. But there is more here too: the need for imagery translates into an economic need because imagery means selling, and cities must always be aware of the need for selling. Buying and selling are basic to our lives. Cities compete for favor (talent, loyalty, money) even as do corporations and individuals.

The need to create a favorable urban image has always existed. Kings built huge monuments to make visual their power. City-states erected extravagant symbols to attract trade and commerce. The bronze statue the "Colossus of Rhodes" was one of the Seven Wonders of the World until destroyed by earthquake in 227 B.C. It could only have been built by a city seeking to express the grandeur of its harbor and thereby attract more commerce. The romantic bridges and quais in Paris reflect a royal demand for beauty. The Ponte Vecchio over the Arno in Italy is now picture-postcard stuff; but the idea of shops on a bridge grew out of the merchants' need to go where the activity was. Venice made its defensive canal system into priceless imagery despite staggering costs of maintenance and preservation. All these costly projects were designed to bring the city glory or profit or, usually, both.

Now, with statistics showing that the average member of our mobile population changes residence every four years, our cities—and our neighborhoods too—must face a struggle for distinction in order to retain and attract consumers (shoppers, industry, taxpayers). Many older, more conservative cities, particularly in the East, seem unaware of the intensity of this competition, their complacency being visually manifested by the deterioration of their "brand image" and their overall unattractiveness. For those who are aware of the economic value of a favorable image, the problem is not *whether* to have an image but rather *what* kind and *how* is it to be achieved.

A few cities have been blessed with natural features of exclusive character that endure and can be enhanced through purposeful urban design. San Antonio, for example, is blessed with a river softly flowing at lower level through the town. The warm Spanish welcome to visitor and tourist is here

Powell Street cable car, San Francisco.

expressed by esplanades and restaurants and the river banked with red-blooming flowers. Pittsburgh, on the other hand, is a dynamic manufacturing center at the conflux of three rivers coursing between rugged hills. Many tunnels and great bridges as early as the Point Bridge of 1825 have created an awesome geometry in the spirit of the Gothic cathedral, and this image of industrial power is reinforced today by the Golden Triangle, a cluster of metallic skyscrapers at river point. San Francisco, built on seven hills like Lisbon, has splendid views of its own and the surrounding hills and the bay. And in the heart of the city the picturesque prevails. The city fathers have seen the commercial value to tourism of appropriate urban furniture in Chinatown; characteristic Oriental shapes have been applied to telephone booths and streetlights. The San Francisco cable cars, thought to be the country's oldest regularly operating transit system, are world-famous. There are thirty-nine of these quaint cars, which operate as a separate municipal railroad division and annually carry 10 million passengers. Each car cost $38,000 but is obviously priceless in terms of contribution to imagery.

Maintaining an image, even an image based on natural assets, is as important as creating one, and as difficult. The importance of Atlantic City and its boardwalk has declined because it has not been reinforced and enhanced. But Carmel, California, has for decades been building and protecting a consistent harmony of natural and man-made scenery. Its incom-

Carmel, California.

Magdalen Street, Norwich, England. Before rehabilitation, 1959.

Magdalen Street, Norwich, England. After rehabilitation, 1959.

46

parable cliffs and beaches along the Pacific have been complemented by the rustic character of all urban furnishings—sidewalks, parking areas, benches, telephone booths, litter baskets. Private developments and shopping centers are in a carefully controlled matching idiom.

When natural endowments are lacking, historical heritage can provide an auspicious approach to unique, time-honored identity, and consumer acceptance. Using as a guide the well-documented Norwich Plan of Norwich, England, several American neighborhoods and shopping streets are being rehabilitated with emphasis on the Victorian character of the streets and houses. Hampton, Virginia, whose renewal program was prepared by Doxiadis Associates, capitalized on a tradition that goes back to the time of the Pilgrims. The imagery of this project has been reinforced by replacing street lighting with antique posts and lanterns imported from England. Similarly, Chicago Old Town, once a decaying cluster of Victorian row houses centered around Wells Street, now presents to the romance-seeking tourist a potpourri of restaurants, pubs, galleries, and shops.

But there isn't enough of the real thing to go around. What of the city that grew up about a fork of the road, hard by a railroad junction, or just by happenstance? The majority of American cities lack natural or historical distinction and in fact are known only by place names and conjure no images to sight or mind. And what of all the new towns and cities still to be built this century? What will be their form and unique identity? With the design talent, technology, and financial resources available today it is possible to construct an "instant tradition" or a "happening environment" in any desired mode where before there was nothing. For example, a city could elect to emulate Disneyland, which may be the greatest piece of urban design in America in terms of commercial performance. But other values are necessary and important to permanent city dwellers, and it is through appraisal and exploitation of these values that every city can and should create its own unique identity.

Cosmetics

The cult of the body is only one manifestation of an American emphasis on personal appearance and youth. Cosmetic products that promise everything to everybody are successfully developed, marketed, and bought. Rapidly changing styles and fashions become more bold and venturesome. And as with men and women, aging cities resort to the use of cosmetics to enhance their public appearance.

The civic consumer is discovering every imaginable gewgaw and nostalgic knickknack of the Victorian era. Gas lamps are in. Redwood planter boxes on Main Street are in. Artificial asters and pansies in baskets hanging over

Main Street, Milpitas, California. Cosmetic planters do not hide overhead wires.

Rockport, Massachusetts. Cosmetic flower baskets do not beautify parking meters.

parking meters are in. Baroque is back. Why? The consumer is unhappy with the ugliness of the old Downtown and the sterility of the new housing developments, and he first turns to cosmetics to blur harsh lines and render fresher-looking the old public face. This popular approach to improvement of community appearance seems quick, easy, and not costly, and many local public-spirited private groups participate in the ritual. A church group will sponsor the boy scouts' cleanup around the neighborhood. The Main Street Merchants Association or local bank or utility will put planter boxes with colorful flowers in the parking lots.

No doubt, in many of these applications the public body, like the human body, profits from cleanliness and some artful enhancement. A canopy of well-cared-for trees, like a bouffant hairdo, can add much charm to a shopping street. But the urban appearance problem usually is more than skin-deep, so that more than cosmetics is needed. These are not a cure, but a palliative, and in that sense deprive the people of the opportunity to achieve a significant and permanent improvement. Indeed, such superficial "medication" may be deadly to civic economic and psychological health if it results in civic self-delusion which delays more painful but effective surgery.

In essence, urban ugliness is likely to be symptomatic of decay, and decay may be malignant, spreading and blighting adjacent healthy areas. Such organic malfunction or disease cannot be arrested or removed by cosmetics. Early diagnosis and basic treatment of the whole organism by professionals is required.

Montreal, Canada. Cosmetic fences conceal slum. Right, they became symbol for protest.

Chapter Three

The
Systems Approach

"No single element in a city is, in truth, the kingpin or the key. The mixture itself is kingpin and its mutual support is the order."
JANE JACOBS

"Most complex systems such as weaponry or space exploration systems are univalent, unipurpose compared to the society that lives in cities. Urban society is indeed a multicomponent, multiinput, multioutput, multipurpose set of structures." WALTER ROSENBLITH, MIT

"Systems . . . are a way of approaching the environment as a total complex organism, of discovering an order which, once established, would preserve those aspects of the environment which we consider essential."
MOSHE SAFDIE

"The systems concept is nothing more than formalized common sense tied to new tools and management methods."

HERBERT H. SWINBRUNE, FAIA

THE CONCEPT
Growth of Systems Analysis

Man-machine systems exist to do work, and they are worth developing only if the work they do cannot easily or correctly be done by man alone. Consequently the machines or equipment in such systems are usually designed to extend man's capabilities or improve his relationship to the environment. Examples are many and obvious. The automobile moves faster than man can run. The hearing aid, first mechanical and now electronic, extends man's ability to hear. Traffic-control devices convey right-of-way data to many people simultaneously. These kinds of man-machine relationships are relatively recent, and their development has largely been trial and error and piecemeal. Street-lighting systems, for example, evolved through many inventions and devices, such as tungsten filaments and transformers. The concept of systems planning, however, is as old as civilization.

The earliest systems engineers were the successful military leaders of legendary campaigns. These aggressive leaders not only had the courage to invade hostile territory but also had the foresight to reconnoitre the size and disposition of opposing forces and use these data to determine the deployment and supply of their own troops. They were military decision makers who considered the complete problem in terms of the total environment.

This commonsense approach remained a nonformalized deductive process through millennia to World War I, which was fought in a static equilibrium of man in trench equalizing man in trench.

But the planning considerations of World War II of necessity changed in response to the altered dimensions and dynamics of opposing forces. Nowadays it is commonplace for planners and designers to start from the outset with a stated desired purpose, or task mission, and create a new totally organized system unlike any other. But the historical literature generally calls the British development of radar the first organized application of systems analysis and design. The accuracy of gunnery had to be improved by as yet unknown machines that would enable the beleaguered British to "see" enemy aircraft far away in the air or submarines deep underwater. Here was a need so desperate the establishment tolerated drastic management measures. Machines called radar resulted from the organized process, in which goals were defined, human needs were expressed, and a technological breakthrough was achieved to make the machines to man's measure. Out of this innovative process a new discipline quickly evolved, complete with vocabulary, modus operandi, and practitioners.

The use of these systems techniques rapidly spread throughout the technical community. Program managers eagerly accepted them because of their usefulness in helping control the increasing number and complexity of variables to be accommodated in reaching viable solutions. Beyond being a means to this end, systems became a design tool as well, a way of getting at problems originally and creatively, disregarding old shibboleths and seeking fresh solutions. Many startling configurations suddenly appeared that successfully accommodated fantastic tasks in weaponry, transportation, and communications. The Bell Aircraft Company's P-39 fighter plane was such a configuration.

The problem at the time was how to get more firepower into the air without sticking more machine guns all along the leading edge of the wings and engine cowling of the fighter plane. Robert Woods, designer of the P-39, achieved an astonishing success using a simple personal procedure of systems analysis.

The P-39.

Since the goal was firepower, not aircraft, Woods first sketched a 39-millimeter cannon, the largest armament yet put into the air. Then he went through systems synthesis, in which the advantages and disadvantages of different possible configurations are swapped back and forth in order to assemble the optimum package. For example, in order not to complicate the rate of fire through the propeller blades, he designed the propeller hub to revolve about the barrel! This advantage, however, had the disadvantage that the cannon was now where the engine normally should be. The designer accepted this, moved the engine further back—behind the cockpit—and created additional space forward into which a nosewheel could be folded, making possible the first military tricycle landing gear. In the process, the designer put the pilot astride the drive shaft, making him interdependent with the systems of armament, propulsion, airframe, and control.

Would man be overwhelmed in the midst of all the machinery? I still vividly recall, from my several hundred hours in the P-39, the oneness I felt with the aircraft when the throbbing crankshaft immediately and closely responded to my touch. There must be, I think, the same sort of rapport between man and motorcycle or man and rocket belt.

Having met wartime challenges, government gave the aerospace industry and its satellite technical suppliers, unfettered by traditional technology, new horizons to conquer. Literally, "Get us to the moon" became the task. The goal was expressed by performance criteria rather than by hardware specifications. Once again faced with the competitive need to produce fantastically complex space-vehicle projects within compressed time schedules, industry turned to systems management and design to meet the performance criteria.

New depersonalized design techniques such as environmental simulation were developed in order to dry-run possible solutions to hazardous or incompletely defined missions. Because of lack of precedence new management procedures were encouraged. Some solved previously insoluble problems; spectacular performance achieved by technical breakthroughs became commonplace. This new know-how found other applications. Consider the V/STOL aircraft.

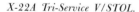

X-22A Tri-Service V/STOL.

Omnidirection aircraft resulted from a new approach to goals previously unattainable. Here the goal was a machine capable not only of vertical takeoff and landing, hovering, and turning 360 degrees but also the forward speed of conventional aircraft. Rather than rehash existing configurations such as rotary wing (helicopter) into unlikely or uneconomical designs, the systems planners devised a new arrangement which imaginatively used fans for both lift and, when rotated, forward thrust. Starting without preconceived notions of what such an airplane should look like, systems analysis produced a wingless four-engine aircraft whose propellers (four fans) point up!

But aircraft and space vehicles are only the beginning. The systems methodology is now affecting millions of people in more immediate and personal ways. It has become vital to the American way of life—in flow of goods to supermarket and to consumer, in the intensive-care systems used in hospitals, in entertainment and communications media such as TV, and in other, still-developing applications to the environment in which we live and work.

Uncommon Use of Common Components

The prevailing practice under which a fragmented bureaucracy specified the styled products of a fragmented industry tended to perpetuate visual pollution. Public products proliferated. Performance criteria were not established for street furniture. User needs were not considered. And producers left to their own devices had little incentive to improve obsolete products; they continued to produce according to the dictates of existing plant and tooling. The cityscape became a junkyard for primitive public equipments.

Meanwhile, in the private building sector, the performance and availability of architectural components improved enormously. Investors wanted bigger buildings cheaper and faster. Industry invested in research and tooling to meet enlarged marketing opportunities. Thousands of new mass-produced systems components offering economy and visual order were produced in the last decade.

The direction of much of this progress was determined by architectural designers. Designers such as Eames and Nelson and design-oriented architectural firms such as Skidmore, Owings & Merrill changed the reproduction approach to furniture and hardware design to an innovative approach which made the article more related to its intended use. Their development of completely new architectural products met the environmental conditions. Sometimes new manufacturing or assembly techniques were required by industry; these had to be developed to produce the design. Often these new components were of such obvious merit they became part of the manufacturer's regular line. These successes spurred similar efforts by other designers. And manufacturers continued to push out the frontiers of machine technology to meet the designers' demand.

In a short time selections of machine-made components that could be imaginatively assembled into a variety of needed building systems became available to all. Storefronts could be assembled at low cost from mass-produced off-the-shelf extrusions produced by several manufacturers. Movable metal office partitions offered new utility and appearance and became an important product line to large building-materials suppliers. The partitions' utility in shaping the interior environment depended largely on the infinite applications made possible through a great number of interrelated factory-made parts such as panels, moldings, clips, etc. Ceiling systems too became a particularly spectacular technical breakthrough. In addition to a selection of texture and form, manufacturers rapidly evolved greater values of flexibility and economy by new relationships to subsystems of illumination, acoustics, and ventilation.

Similar success accrued in storage walls with interchangeable panels, display systems with universal connectors and most importantly with exterior wall systems. Curtain walls could now package larger and larger building spaces. Using metal or synthetic factory-made materials, these components promoted flexibility of arrangement and size, allowable tolerance for field assembly, and a precise geometric configuration which facilitated self-positioning and locking. Their obvious esthetic and technical merit and their prefabricated economy promoted quick consumer acceptance by developers as well as designers.

The market for these building components was swiftly enlarged by the simplicity of use and the implied low level of skill or small amount of time necessary to arrive at serviceable and economical applications. These well-designed components could be assembled by almost everyone in an appropriate manner. And in the hands of a talented designer who sometimes arranged the standard parts in unexpected ways, the unexpected effect could be unique and intriguing.

Now other dramatic ideas are being proposed for all aspects of building technology, so that today most visually exciting developments seem to be those structures designed as a system of standardized parts whose arrangement does the job better and also creates novel spatial and visual relationships. Housing is undergoing an industrialized change, from site construction by hand labor to volume production by machine and unskilled factory labor. Innovators are now conceiving even more sophisticated systems which have in common the use of repetitive load-bearing or functional modules and components to achieve simplified site installation unobtainable by conventional building design.

Williamsville Pool Club, Amherst, New York. Prefabricated dressing rooms. Several hundred plugged into concrete floor in varying arrangements.

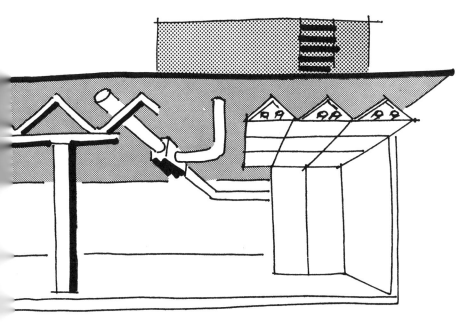

School Construction Systems Development (SCSD) was the definitive study in the field of systems building.

United States Pavilion, Expo 67, Montreal.

Habitat, Expo 67, Montreal.

The City as a System

The industrial revolution resulted in the machine's replacing muscle as a way of life. It became commonplace to think of machines as aids to perceiving and manipulating and making more enjoyable the environment. These new devices helped man to see in the dark, to make himself heard at great distance, to speed over great distances.

Rapidly the production of light evolved from lamp to lighting system, then became a power-distribution system. The telephone changed from voice-transmitting tool to conceptually sophisticated communication system. The airplane changed from a marginal-performance novelty to a utilitarian transportation system complete with terminals and controlled air routes. The accelerated development and acceptance of beneficial systems is probably the most spectacular technical accomplishment of our age. All these examples are man-made synthetic organisms. And just as the factory has become a system, so also is the city a system.

Each of course contains subsystems. The automated factory may have production lines. It also may be structured and framed with systems components; its interior spaces are analyzed and ordered; its environment is controlled by networks of communications, air conditioning, snow removal, fire control, and smoke warning.

The city, shopping center, or campus may contain similar subsystems. These environments must have systems of lighting, fire protection, and traffic control in order to be considered secure, healthful, and economically viable. Street-highway, pedestrian-sidewalk, and automobile-parking systems must be considered. No one system is independent of the others.

To make the city appreciably more useful and desirable, not one but all systems with significant relationships must be considered and upgraded. In truth, the urban community can be looked upon as a complex system of related functional activities directed toward meeting all the needs of its people. The functional areas of importance to every individual are the standard of living, housing, well-being and recreation, and support for the first three.

The importance of public facilities as support for these private, personal needs lies far beyond the obviously necessary environmental services such as sewers and water supply, power and transportation, and lighting and guidance. There are other values. As instrumentalities for community identity and appearance, urban furnishings are without peer. Since street furnishings include all visible physical surfaces, textures, and equipments in the public space, from the private building line to the center of the street, they *are* the public environment. Since they are largely machine-made, the urban fabric *is* synthetic.

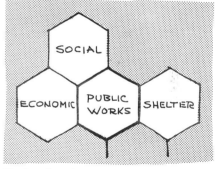

The interface of site improvements and community factors.

At less cost, this fabric can be designed and produced with imagination and artistry. Or it can remain dull, unimaginative, and inadequate in representing the best in a city's character.

In most cities of America, unlike Europe, there is little concern for how urban furnishings determine community appearance. Presently there is no office or agency charged with a design function and authority to coordinate the various fragmented jurisdictions and interests. The few attempts to cope with city imagery have been piecemeal solutions to nonbasic problems. Most attempts at furnishing the city are more tried than true. For example, if Downtown looks gray and dingy, then more lampposts are installed; if traffic is congested, then the streets are widened at the expense of the sidewalks; if neighborhood streets are shabby, then they are covered with fresh asphalt.

But furnishing the city and creating a unique environment are not that simple. For now the important thing is not to have more of the same kind of hardware, but to adopt an approach oriented toward broader objectives. Then the most immediate benefits will accrue from an analysis of all community appearance factors in their relationships with each other. Street paving, for example, is now to be considered not only in relation to vehicular traffic but also in context with graphics and markings and pedestrian crossways and as a floor for other furniture.

A basic problem in very many American cities is the lack of community identity and values sufficient to induce a sense of belonging or caring. The problem is not so much the shabbiness of the city as its lack of vitality and dilution of enjoyment. The old ethnic neighborhoods have had their distinctions diluted and destroyed without replacement by other characteristics of equal flavor. This basic problem will not be solved with new architectural monuments, whether bland and sterile or aggressive and dynamic. The nature of the problem requires people-oriented goals, which tend to require a completely new or rehabilitated product (environment) of such unique and desirable character as to stimulate public desire for ownership or participation. People must want to work for, to treasure, to enjoy a piece of the city—*their* city.

Another need is to put a "price" on the space allotted to competing city-department users. Generally the public space is regarded as a free "good;" thus it is used by city departments at will without regard for productivity. To establish goals and tasks for the space and "charge" for the space would provide an incentive for comparing the efficiency of various city departments. It might then become necessary for departments to justify use of space and therefore optimize the size and efficiency of their equipments within the space. It has even been suggested that the bureaucracy within each department should "pay rent" from the department budget for each unit of public space it uses.

THE METHODOLOGY

How It Works

In systems design for industry there are as many variations in procedure as practitioners. Various requirements of different applications such as construction planning or communications design mandate flexibility of approach. In environmental design the methodology is even less well defined, since the number of purposeful applications has been extremely limited.

This is all right, because the essential thing about systems thinking is that it is freewheeling. In systems thinking, unlike the mechanistic Bauhaus or the international "ism" schools of design, there is no cookbook of forms or dogmatic attitude toward design. There are no preconceived notions about what is and what is not good design. The designer can be more genuinely and freely experimental. He is free to move and develop with social as well as technical changes.

The systems approach is fundamentally a decision-making process. It considers alternative approaches to overall design to provide optimum performance. It is best suited to dynamic problems where inputs or conditions vary. The systems approach does start, however, with the proposition that in order for a highly complex arrangement of objects, people, and space to be optimally designed, the process of decision making must be placed on a rational and objective basis. Any successful methodology for getting at solutions to the problems of human needs that are involved must be an organized procedure.

The accompanying chart depicts such a procedure, including the principal phases and flow of a typical work program. For the sake of clarity of applica-

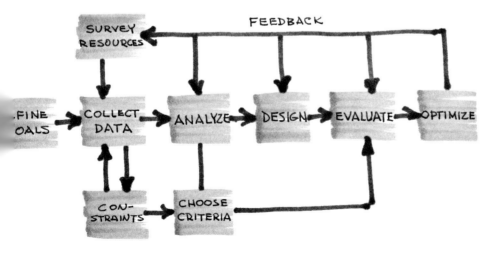

tion the procedure may be considered in the context of a hypothetical problem: how to furnish and unify a neighborhood renewal project containing 50 percent older structures, 50 percent new housing, new open spaces, and old streets and stores.

Definition of Problem, Establishment of Goals   First decide what needs to be done in general terms. The objectives must be broad enough so as not to predetermine solutions. Only the crucial issues should be formalized. These should be expressed in terms of user requirements so that the statement of goals is one which clearly considers the human values of the society in which the new system will perform. Example: for nighttime, the best way to unify the project is through a programmed lighting sequence, not just through deciding how many lampposts to install.

This statement of goals becomes the mandate, the charter, authorizing and approving the scope of effort, and should be approved and adopted as law by the community legislative body. With this authority the design guidelines can be activated and take precedence when existing building codes or minimum-specification guides come into conflict.

Data Collection   Program implementation starts with the collection of raw data by means of a systematic survey. The condition of things is recorded. City engineering and public works departments are a source of data on quantity and condition of existing public improvements in the area. This material can be tabulated. Information should also be collected on both the positive and the negative factors that may affect the program. Example: *Constraints* may include state codes, marginal bond capacity, inadequate public works budget, adverse features of climate or of street shape and size. *Resources* may include state or local funds that can be marshaled, new technology, interested private developers, community or businessmen's associations.

An important part of this input is the visual survey, which establishes the existing quality of the environment. The purpose of the survey is to note elements which can be capitalized and other elements which should be written off. These assets and liabilities are noted in terms of *consumer acceptance,* not architectural context. The analyst must say in his mind, "I am standing waiting for a bus. How do I feel? I am sitting in my car waiting for the traffic light to change. What do I see? I am walking on the sidewalk. What are its width, color, and condition?"

Every section of a city differs from any other and creates its own atmosphere, or local color. This may be either positive or negative, by attracting or repelling people. Sometimes commonplace features such as bridges, water towers, and street patterns which are different from those in other areas of the city can be accentuated and made to be beneficial landmarks orienting pedestrian and motorist as well as providing character.

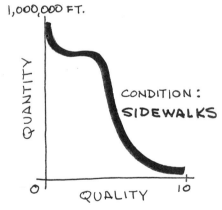

Site-improvements profile.

Among the several references on visual-survey techniques Paul Spreiregen presents the most rounded summary. He stresses that the survey should disclose where the area needs reshaping, and he mentions that a visual survey can be made of any town and at different scales, such as the neighborhood. Other writers, planners, and landscape architects have presented various techniques of observation, notation, and image mapping. Many of these tend to be highly abstract and arcane. As Spreiregen points out, the results ought to be presented in maps and photographs and in everyday terms easily understood by everyone.

Actually the fieldwork can be recorded in any shorthand form. The difficulty with visual-survey technique is the lack of understanding or definition of what is a common visual language. Once what has been seen has been recorded by whatever notation, the problem remains of how the personal, subjective views are to be interpreted and applied.

Analysis The third step is really a process ongoing with data collection. Questions and curiosity stimulate thinking; good ideas may occur during the visual survey. As a conscious procedure in this phase the subproblems of the environmental system are identified and analyzed. The design parameters and relationships of components one to the other are established. Example: Decide how people of this neighborhood use the public right-of-way and spaces. Consider what kinds of facilities and imagery are required. Establish what interrelationships of form, color, materials, scale, and graphics are desired. Prepare new standards and performance criteria for each subsystem (floor, lighting, litter control) and information for evaluation of possible solutions.

Synthesis This design phase develops specific solutions, which should deal in an innovative way with all the forces discovered to be relevant in the previous phases. Esthetics should not be consciously contrived. In order to meet the initial goals, they should result from the manipulation of existing forms, shapes, and products and all environmental features that interrelate. A number of specific concepts can be proposed that resolve the initially stated objectives of unification. Example: unify the neighborhood by means of a strong identifiable floor pattern with a collector strip between curb and sidewalk, gathering and organizing the street-furniture subsystems.

Optimization In this process we select pieces of possible solutions and give up others in order to put together the most economical harmonious whole. Trade-offs are made; in a process of bargaining or compromising among subsystems with a view to enhancing the overall conglomerate performance. Various ideas are culled; the alternatives are weighed against evaluation criteria. The fundamental value consideration in choosing a design option is ratio of performance to cost of design chosen. But performance may have to be measured by a sizable variety of criteria, which will not necessarily be compatible with each other. Furthermore emphasis changes. For example, Ian McHarg and others stress the increasing importance of social benefit as a significant value factor in evaluating alternate highway routes.

In light of new national aspirations and social goals, livability joins and must be traded off against other "ilities"—maintainability, reliability, and so on. The weight of livability in the cost/benefit formula will vary among various environmental systems, such as traffic control, lighting, and fire protection, but its inclusion to some degree is now essential.

During optimization a model of the overall system is used to clarify and test the proposed solutions. Systems engineering and operations research makes much use of *mathematical models* as a relatively inexpensive way to dry-run expensive configurations. The more variables and possible choices, the more useful are computer techniques. The computer has been used by highway designers in cut-and-fill calculations for many years. And its structural-design potential was dramatically demonstrated at Expo 67 when the huge Gyrotron space structure was calculated in two days of computer time instead of four million man-hours. This imitation reality is a quick way to identify what needs to be measured and then measure it.

Mathematical models are organized logically. Their language and structure are those of symbolic logic, which simplifies reality and eliminates unessential considerations. The organization is rigorous, and assumptions are clearly stated. These basic principles can be applied well to the creative field of urban design. Planners have not yet made much use of mathematical models, probably because they have not had on hand the information needed to make them useful. In fact, automated information systems and mathematical models will develop together, as pointed out in a recent study on urban planning data systems by Campbell and LeBlanc. As more data, including graphic material on aperture cards, are captured in automated data processing systems, planners will be able to construct mathematical models and use them to better advantage.

Meanwhile much use is made of *visual models,* which are organized spatially. Whether three-dimensional, a map, or a photograph, the model has scale, and scale tends to simplify subsystem relationships for visualization. Things can be left out, or they can be overstated. The visual model can also be used to test out the design economically by altering features or substituting new features for old.

Many leading architectural firms use *illustrative site plans* to articulate major public improvements and demonstrate unifying elements. The interplay of public areas and facilities can be graphically shown by detailing, for example, pedestrian-channelization features such as walks, ramps, platforms, concourses, and arcades. The relationships of these elements to open-space

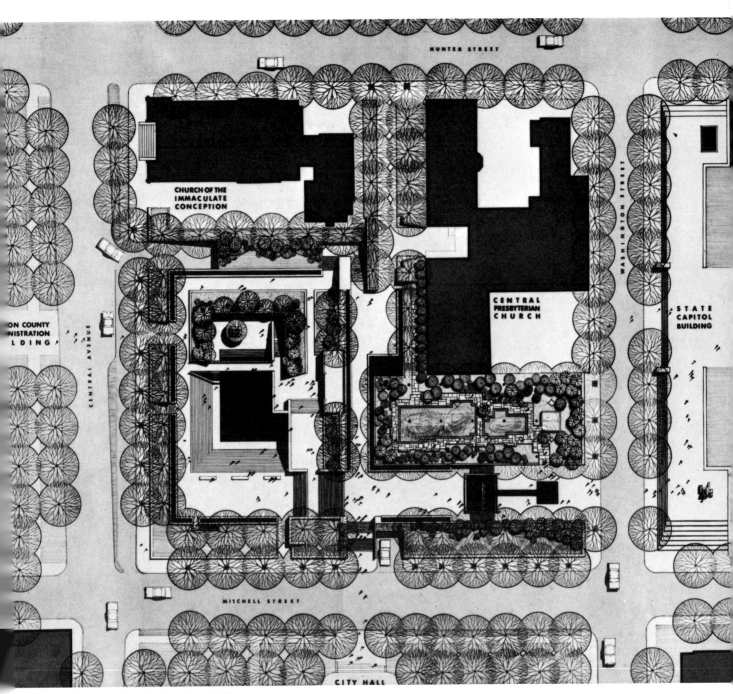

HUNTER STREET

CHURCH OF THE
IMMACULATE
CONCEPTION

CENTRAL
PRESBYTERIAN
CHURCH

STATE
CAPITOL
BUILDING

ON COUNTY
NISTRATION
LDING

CENTRAL AVENUE

WASHINGTON STREET

MITCHELL STREET

CITY HALL

Illustrative site plan for Georgia Plaza.
Atlanta, Georgia.

*Study model for Georgia Plaza (scale : ⅛″
1′0″). Model helps develop design, working
drawings, full-size mock-up.*

features such as plazas, pools, and landscaping as well as to service parking systems can be illustrated. Areas planned for social and community activities such as happenings, parades, and concerts can be visualized in proper relationships.

But frequently the feel of the street furnishings in relationship with urban spaces can be better worked out in three-dimensional models. The models used are similar to models of industrial complexes, such as chemical plants with intricate piping crossovers and configurations. An environmental model need not represent each component in such expensive literal fashion but should facilitate plug-in of design changes rather than be merely a static presentation medium. Further, environmental simulation by means of enclosures into which the observer looks through low-elevation human-scale peepholes will be more meaningful than tabletop models which are viewed from above with Olympian detachment.

In addition, when street-furniture components are to be mass-produced, the cost of full-size mock-ups is warranted in order to optimize design, consider environmental scale, and anticipate production problems.

Whichever mode is selected, the model may be used to perform several functions: to clarify solutions, demonstrate cost/benefit relationships, test alternate combinations, and pick up interface or side-effect problems.

The resulting flow of information is distributed into the design process by means of "feedback." This term defines an important part of the design process whereby part of the output (information on solutions) is returned as input (design data) to the continuing systems development. As various parts of the project progress, these communications help ensure that the overall design is in balance.

The final step in systems methodology is to put the optimum configuration into action. This too is a systematic procedure and is discussed later in greater detail.

SYSTEMS DEVELOPMENT

Project Planning and Control

Sound project management is essential to any complex enterprise. It is perhaps most critical to the orderly progression of urban systems work, in consideration of the complexity of relationships between local city departments, outside agencies, consultants, and contractors. Because of the public nature of the work, a constant dialogue must be maintained between the urban planner, designer, and city administration. Communication between designer and contractor, lost since the days of direct feedback between master builder and craftsman, must be restored. When problems arise, there must be a means for presentation of alternates for reaching previously established goals. In short, the project manager must control the project through a number of phases of design, estimating, purchasing, contracting, quality control, installation, and support.

In the past decade three things have drastically increased the work burden of the project manager:

More Projects Definite unique goals must be met by specific target dates.

Increased Size and Complexity More technical problems involve more services and agencies and require more reports.

Increased Time Pressure Target dates imposed by others require the manager to optimize resources of men, money, and machines.

Thus more and more the manager has to think in generalities. He cannot always be aware of all details; he cannot even be aware of all activities which are critical. Clearly, what is needed is a master model which shows the overall planning picture. The systems methodology inherently offers not only this but also an orderly procedure for the organized management and control of the project: configuration management can maintain the integrity of the system as it is shaped by many hands.

Several techniques derived from the needs of, and compatible with, systems design have evolved very recently. These replace the conventional master plan featuring a bar chart which listed milestones and required subjective estimates of percentage of work completed. The newer project planning systems tend to be self-maintaining and provide uniform display and interpretation while in concurrent use by city, consultant, and contractor or vendor.

Network planning provides the discipline within which design activities can be organized and the development process controlled. According to the AIA publication *Emerging Techniques of Architectural Practice,* most formats presently favored are adaptations or combinations of one of two network planning systems, program evaluation and review technique and the critical-path method.

Program evaluation and review technique (PERT) evolved through military systems needs; the first large-scale application was the Polaris missile program for the Navy in the late 1950s, when the efforts of some thirty-eight hundred participating groups were coordinated. The program was event-oriented; that is, certain milestones were set up as events that had to take place at certain times. The activities were compressed as required between events.

Now many models are activity-oriented; that is, the activities are diagramed so that no activity begins until the preceding jobs have been completed. Only after the project has been planned with this logic is time associated with activities, connecting nodes, or events.

The critical-path method (CPM) is simple in concept—a graphic presentation in which everything gets a label. Complete projects are reduced to diagrams in which arrows show the flow of work, one arrow representing a single activity or task. Several methods may be used to indicate the time consumed by each activity on the diagram. One way is to start the arrow with a beginning number, indicating that the project has to be that far along before that activity may begin, and an ending number to show at what point in the project's time the activity will conclude. Another number is assigned to show the duration in time of the particular task.

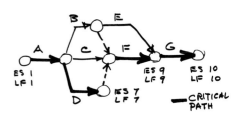

Two questions to ask in creating a critical-path diagram are these: "When must this particular activity be started?" and "When must it be completed to allow the next activity to begin?" Often one task will be preceded by several arrows, all of which must be completed before beginning the new job.

The critical path through the arrow network is the one which takes the longest time sequence to complete. It shows the shortest possible time in which the project may be completed. Paths can move up, down, and sideways. Paths of shorter duration have slack time available along the way since none is as time-consuming as the critical path. This slack time is called "float." Total float is the amount of time that any activity can be delayed without delaying the entire project. It is computed by subtracting the time required for the activity from the time available to accomplish it. Float time can be borrowed from noncritical activities and used as job conditions dictate to cut project time and control manpower.

Because the relationship of one activity to another is known, the CPM permits all participants to see trouble immediately and know how the overall project is affected by slippage in any particular activity. And the CPM can be updated periodically, thus presenting a constantly accurate model.

Project Development

The essence of systems design of public improvements is the concurrent design and procurement of all anticipated components necessary to satisfy the project goals. Conventional previous practice required public facilities to be developed in a piecemeal manner. First the street pattern would be planned; subsequently a lighting pattern would be drawn; traffic controls would be considered after the street was in use; and possibly at some time in the future parking controls, trash collection, and amenities like landscaping might be considered. This procedure cannot achieve proper interface of all major subsystems required for a simplified and less costly community appearance.

The State University Construction Fund of New York, recently faced with

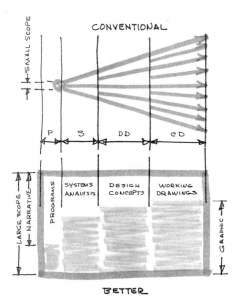

CONVENTIONAL

SMALL SCOPE

P · S · DD · CD

LARGE SCOPE

NARRATIVE

PROGRAMS | SYSTEMS ANALYSIS | DESIGN CONCEPTS | WORKING DRAWINGS

GRAPHIC

BETTER

Parallel pattern development.

the task of planning and constructing some 1.5 billion dollars worth of new and rehabilitated campuses in the decade ending in 1970, evolved a number of design and management techniques under the direction of Anthony G. Adinolfi. This was possibly the first civilian bureaucracy oriented toward using contemporary management techniques to achieve massive public works of contemporary design. One campus alone (Buffalo), when completed in the mid-1970s, will be a 700-million-dollar planned community second in scope to none except possibly Brasilia. The program management techniques developed here have broad application in other areas of community improvement, even those of much lesser scope. One of the most useful techniques is parallel pattern development.

The principle has been established that to secure a balanced project design, all elements of the design must be considered initially and at each subsequent phase of the development. A gradual increase in detail of development across the board is desired even though emphasis changes from phase to phase. This requires that the initial scope be complete and a broad design concept be pursued from the onset.

The accompanying diagrams compare project development techniques. The upper chart describes the conventional process, starting with a narrow scope and developing the design by trial and error. The lower chart describes the parallel process, in which the initial scope, goals, program, functional requirements, and site and spatial requirements are complete and do not change. An orderly progression can thus be made through the schematic design and detailed drawing stages.

Prior to conceptualizing, the designer must receive from the administration (developer, management) all programs. In the case of a specific campus these could be presented in a document containing topics such as "Education Plan" and "Enrollment Plan." The former would list goals, policies, and assumptions—for example, philosophy and purpose of campus, programs offered, evening and community use. The latter might contain statements on present enrollment, anticipated enrollments by target dates, and student/faculty ratios.

The designer could then analyze these in terms of physical need for academic, dining, housing, circulation, and sports spaces and facilities, for instance. Facilities could in turn be analyzed in relationship to the site and the community and region. And finally, before actual design an economic analysis should be made to determine a meaningful budget estimate for the complete program through its target date.

Parallel development applies also to all stages subsequent to planning and design, including manufacturing. Once the overall configuration has been fixed, the system can be fractured into each major subsystem, or component, for development and production. However, each component would be in a controlled parallel path so as to be available for reintegration at the necessary time.

PUTTING THE TECHNIQUES TO WORK

Example: Campus Information System

Task: A completely new academic community with a projected full-time student population of 30,000 plus faculty, staff, and visitors requires parking regulation, motorist and pedestrian guidance, and building and space identification. The site is a 400-acre tract in Albany, New York. The designer is consultant to the architect, Edward Durell Stone and Associates; the client is the State University Construction Fund of New York.

Problem: The architectural complex is very homogeneous. The dormitory and academic buildings are not identifiable by shape, scale, or color. They are nearly identical structures positioned uniformly on vast podia. Therefore, on one hand, a great need exists for signage of visibility, legibility, and identity. But on the other hand, it is desired that the street furniture be minimal, neutral, and nonobtrusive. The problem is to organize an information system that communicates in a manner that satisfies both criteria.

Solution: Phase 1: Collect data on campus circulation, proposed location of facilities, and their uses. Make a visual survey. Simulate activity of a stranger in the environment. Enter the campus, park car, walk grounds (buildings and site work incomplete). Visualize needs of motorist and pedestrian for information. Determine needs of administration for control and regulation. Compile list of anticipated messages for signage.

Phase 2: Analyze information needs in context of use of spaces and architectural environment. Determine degree of visibility required, which in turn will establish scale of letter forms and panels. Consider suitability of materials. Determine tentative locations of graphic elements on site plan.

Concurrently establish performance criteria for evaluation of future designs. Typical criteria are:

a Greatest utility with fewest number of components.
b Compatibility in color and symmetry of form to the very ordered architecture.
c Minimum size consistent with legibility.
d Resistance to vandalism.

Phase 3: Design a conceptual model containing the following interrelated subsystems in order of visitor need:

a Traffic-control system (signals, signs, pavement markings) for safe exit from two major and five minor highway intersections into the campus road network and to parking lots (STOP, GO).
b Campus directories which graphically provide position orientation to motorists at each of six entrances to campus (YOU ARE HERE).

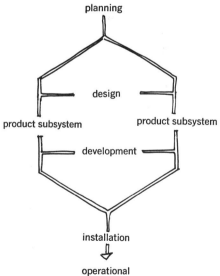

Parallel development of project.

71

Precast Wall System

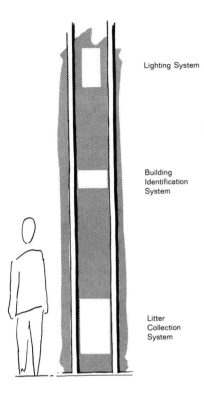

Lighting System

Building
Identification
System

Litter
Collection
System

c   Motorist-guidance system alongside roadways which directs motorists to parking lots (PARK THERE).
d   Pedestrian-guidance system alongside walks which graphically directs pedestrian to each of several architectural complexes.
e   Building-identification system that relates to the architecture (as hardware). This subsystem interfaces with the building curtain-wall subsystem in scale and mounting position and also to the overhead wall-mounted lighting system for illumination.
f   Campus-activity identification system (portable guidance).

Phase 4: Develop the designs after approval of concept. Fracture into manageable parts. Process the various subassemblies and components under parallel development, in which the design of each is refined and detailed to the procurement and installation stage, where they reunite. Standardize sign framing for all systems. Standardize sign-panel sizes and materials. Standardize color codes (reverse white letters on umber background for motorist signs, black and white on umber for pedestrian and motorist campus directories). Standardize size of letters. Design and adapt house-style alphabets (Standard Medium alphabet for motorist, Caslon for pedestrian signs). Standardize placement of signs and prepare location diagrams.

Phase 5: Optimize through trade-offs and realignment. Evaluate against selection and performance criteria. Make composite site plan of all subsystems. Simplify and reduce number of mounting and installation variations. Eliminate marginal units. Check for side-effect problems such as competition with nearby lampposts or reduced visibility of signs because of landscaping.

Phase 6: Become operational. Select vendors and proceed through bidding process. Monitor subsystems through fabrication period. Install and test

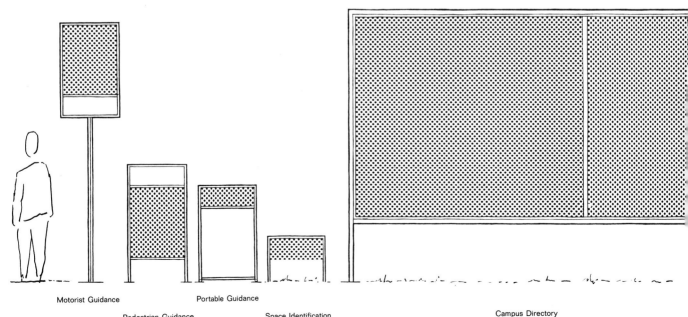

Motorist Guidance

Portable Guidance

Pedestrian Guidance

Space Identification

Campus Directory

components. Prepare *Campus Graphics Manual* that describes systems purposes, procedurizes and standardizes operations for administrative personnel, and specifies maintenance procedures for use by shop personnel.

SOME SYSTEMS LAWS FOR DESIGNERS

Let the Problem Program the Solution

Most public works programs, Downtown remodeling projects, airport programs, housing developments in the ghetto, and so on start with too limited and detailed a proposal. The larger the area to which programs and goals pertain, the greater the chances for implementation. Big beautiful plans capture the imagination and help get the needed support for execution. In the thirteenth century Kublai Khan inspired (or admonished, as was a custom with potentates) his boldest men to great efforts. "To build a beautiful city," he said, "we must start with a beautiful concept." Wisely, he did not specify an architectural form in the program for the city of Peking that he advanced to his philosophers and artists. The form evolved from the broad mandate to create a beautiful way of life in a new city. In the more contemporary towns of Europe and in the new American towns of Columbia and Reston, by contrast, the forms have evolved from uncompromised considerations of how shopping might be best done, how close people should live to each other and to the civic centers, etc.

A conceptual model is sometimes made in the systems analysis phase as an aid to defining the problem. Consider the realignment of a street system connecting three nodes equidistant from each other, as shown in the illustration on page 75. If the primary objective of the network is to provide a minimum of travel between points, the street system (B) will result. If the primary objective is to provide a minimal total street mileage at reduced cost, the network (A) will prevail. If the main objective is to preserve a historic monument or landmark, then the street pattern (C) will be followed. Thus the conceptual model must reflect the characteristics of the real systems which are to be investigated.

Environmental design, then, is not valid unless it has relationship to the complete basic problem. Example: A strip shopping plaza begins to have store vacancies and is unwanted by tenants on any terms. The developer might go to a designer and say, "Look, we are losing too much business. Do something about this. Put a bigger and more rustic-looking sign on the parking lot, and color all the facades green." The designer's problem then would not be how to make the strip plaza more acceptable to people, but how to design a more rustic sign. Obviously this is incorrect, because it is not a sign or the color of storefronts that is keeping people away, and it may be the layout of the parking areas or the inconvenience of going from store to store in the rain and snow. The solution to those major problems might better be said to be to create a new circulation pattern or some means of climate control.

Or should the solution to the problems of the shopping area be expressed as follows:

1. Put in parking meters to open up more spaces to bring more visitors in cars?

2. Increase nighttime brilliance with more footcandles of light?

3. Widen the street to reduce traffic congestion? Not a very good approach. These are all possible solutions, but not broad enough objectives. They are all commonly used and frequently ineffective. The basic problem was not adequately assessed, and therefore the solutions are inadequate. Creative thinking is forestalled and frozen.

Making everyone in the community want to shop there should be the basic goal. This kind of problem formulation requires broader conceptual thinking and tolerates the expression of more innovative proposals and alternatives. Many interlocked areas of planning must then be considered. Some design goals might be:

1. Generate more pedestrian-shopper activity with exciting entertainment, recreational, cultural, or civic facilities.

2. Create a new landmark symbol (or restore a historical heritage) to provide a sense of place and identifying trademark.

3. Create a new environmental package or reinforce an indigenous neighborhood character by redesigning the street, using a comprehensive concept that emphasizes its distinction.

This approach is deductive; in it the designer works from the general to the specific. The viewpoint is wide and not focused on narrow objectives which lead to small solutions. The design concepts are based on the broadest possible terms that can be conceived and presented.

To consider another case, the design of a neighborhood housing project should relate to metropolitan or regional programs and possibilities. The concepts should be independent of existing boundaries, thinking, codes, practices. The definition of the scope of design should be as broad as possible, though the definition of the area of action will be limited to the area of jurisdiction.

If such a task seems difficult because as many as five different city agencies may be involved in the physical and administrative considerations of community appearance, then perhaps *this* is the problem. The goal then lies not in avoiding the problem or temporizing or accepting a weak design. The desirability for change of city administrative codes and procedures to permit the adoption and use of a desirable design becomes self-evident.

Components Should Complement the Big Concept

Designers know that many forces are always chipping away at big visions, frequently cutting them down from heroic to less than life size. Systems design in which all components move forward concurrently and are interdependent tend to resist this abrasive action more strongly. To weaken one element means the degradation of all systems performance.

To ensure that all components are properly developing during the design process, the original program statement of requirements should be periodically reviewed and updated if necessary. Checkpoints should be built into the planning process and component designs constantly reviewed and evaluated against the overall environmental systems program.

The following criteria apply:

1. Good systems design works for and pleases people. Products or urban furnishings should not overwhelm the user.

2. The various components should do a better job collectively than separately. Example: a graphics system should be more effective than uncoordinated random signs.

3. Products should be related in scale, materials, and form to each other and the larger environmental expression.

4. Products must also have self-identifying characteristics. Components should have an exciting quality that helps build the total image. Each can have individuality yet serve to unify the environment.

5. Components should be planned more for flexibility than exactitude. Exterior spaces change and serve many uses. No public improvements are inviolate or permanent. Streets get resurfaced. Lighting needs increase.

Nonsense Input Produces Shrdlu

When the operator of a linotype machine fingers incomprehensible data into the machine, he gets back a type slug which says "shrdlu." Urban designers are not that fortunate. They have no fail-safe device to signal faulty input.

Basically, the ultimate goal of all decisions in community appearance design is to maximize the desired outcome. Since many real decision situations have many nonquantitive (esthetic) variables, they are too complex to be treated mathematically. It is often necessary to introduce simplifying assumptions by considering only the variables, relationships, and objectives that are deemed to be important by the decision maker.

System synthesis is the initial conception of a street-furniture system the purpose of which is to satisfy certain human needs. In order to make an intelligent selection of alternatives, designers are often required to specify design and operation criteria, study system properties, propose alternative schemes, and assess technological and economic feasibility.

In setting up the task, it is important to select a conceptual model which expresses the appropriate relationship of public facilities to the environmental needs. Therefore, identifying proper variables to feed into the conceptual model is one of the most important phases of the entire creative process. The importance of correct judgment in assessing this input to a proposed design project cannot be overemphasized. If an incorrect premise is assumed, no amount of creative discipline or elegance of design can save the resulting system from the error of misjudgment.

At present, urban data collection, processing, and evaluation do not constitute a rigorous procedure with a rigorous set of terms or definitions. There is no common language, no standard methodology, no uniform format for information gathering and processing. Controls are lacking to ensure the accuracy and validity of assumptions used to construct esthetic and visual systems in the cityscape.

Obviously, the assessment of project parameters depends largely on the sensitivity of the designer to critical features. Techniques need to be developed which assist in the evaluation by others of these conditions as both a fail-safe device and a model of existing or proposed conditions.

Evaluation criteria used to compare alternatives in design development.

	least									most
	1	2	3	4	5	6	7	8	9	10
1. Flexibility to site conditions										
2. Structural Efficiency										
3. Other Component Compatibility										
4. Simplicity										
5. Technological Feasibility										
6. Maintainability										
7. Life–Cost Benefit										
8. Community Identity										
9. User Efficiency/Convenience										
10. Public Safety/Street Utilization										

Total Score _____

One recent successful experiment along these lines was the Metropolitan Data Center Project, funded under a 1966 demonstration grant of the Renewal Assistance Administration (RAA). The purpose was to apply the capabilities of data processing equipment and techniques to planning problems. The project was concerned with the storage and analysis of information concerning land use, housing, and environmental factors. One cooperating agency, the Wichita-Sedgwick County Metropolitan Area Planning Commission, Wichita, Kansas, used a computer program which analyzed the capital-improvement programming alternatives. This developed methods for establishing priorities and balancing subjective judgments as to the proper course of action. Essential to the success of the project was the format of the document used to capture input data for the computer.

PROJECT FACTORS
PRIORITY DETERMINANTS
PARK PROJECTS

---

1. Evaluate the recreational value of the project in terms of its tendency to serve the citizenry with respect to each of the following

	Minor									Major
• physical well being	1	2	3	4	5	6	7	8	9	10
• mental and emotional health	1	2	3	4	5	6	7	8	9	10
• intellectual development	1	2	3	4	5	6	7	8	9	10
• ability to organize and carry responsibility	1	2	3	4	5	6	7	8	9	10
• character development	1	2	3	4	5	6	7	8	9	10
• social adjustment	1	2	3	4	5	6	7	8	9	10
• aesthetic and spiritual values	1	2	3	4	5	6	7	8	9	10
• values to society	1	2	3	4	5	6	7	8	9	10
• community attractiveness	1	2	3	4	5	6	7	8	9	10
• civic spirit	1	2	3	4	5	6	7	8	9	10
• education for democracy	1	2	3	4	5	6	7	8	9	10
• safety	1	2	3	4	5	6	7	8	9	10
• economy	1	2	3	4	5	6	7	8	9	10

---

2. Extent of value of proposed project as aesthetic improvement for a major part of the city.

1 2 3 4 5 6 7 8 9 10
None   Very Great

---

3. Special value of proposed project as deterrent to crime or delinquency.

1 2 3 4 5 6 7 8 9 10
None   Very Great

---

4. If proposed improvement is made, by what extent (%) will the facility/population ratio be above the accepted minimum?

1 2 3 4 5 6 7 8 9 10
0-10%   90-100%

---

5. If proposed improvement is made, by what extent (%) will the facility/population ratio be below the accepted minimum?

1 2 3 4 5 6 7 8 9 10
0-10%   90-100%

---

6. To what extent is this project a creation of new park-recreation facilities as opposed to improvement of existing facilities?

1 2 3 4 5 6 7 8 9 10
None   Very Great

---

7. To what extent is this project essential to preserve natural resources for public use and to prevent its early development for private use?

1 2 3 4 5 6 7 8 9 10
None   Very Great

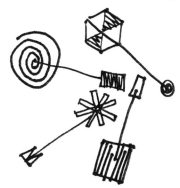
Uncoordinated chaos

Modular coordination

Systems-sharing matrix

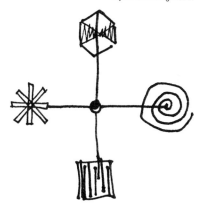

Various coordinating methods compared.

One Plus One Equals Three

The functional purpose of systems design is to make the whole greater than the sum of the parts. This synergism has value in urban design as in any other design situation of complexity involving many bits and pieces. No one doubts the existence of the terrible clutter of signs, products, and other "things" in the cityscape. Architects have always been sensitive to this kind of esthetic horror. Yet the vast synergetic benefit possible through consolidating these environmental components is hardly recognized.

This synergetic benefit will be secured through systems sharing—support, energy, form, envelope. Instead of self-contained relationships, an interdependence must be created between elements that constitute the product environment. When it is created, the resultant coalition structure not only is stronger and accommodates greater tasks than a competitive structure but also is less costly. The result is a higher payoff per element; we get higher performance per pound. Examples: several electrically actuated subsystems can be fed from one power-supply system; more passengers can be transported in a mass-transit vehicle than in private cars; many equipments can utilize the same post on a street corner; a large church congregation can share the parking lot of an adjacent plaza or department store on Sundays or during nonconflicting hours.

Frequently this increased value is achieved through systematic reduction in the number of discrete elements. Example: A mass-transit vehicle replaces forty cars. The reduced expenditure of resources (cost of highway construction, loss of private-property tax base) results in lower cost per unit (passenger-miles). With the constantly increasing competition for funds to furnish the city, coalition planning and design of street furnishings provide a way to make available money go further.

Moreover, products are not cheapened, but simplified and improved. In this sense the approach has similarities to value engineering, in which proposed or existing designs are evaluated for possible simplification and cost reduction in manufacture. The advantage in applying this to systems analysis is that the benefits are built in beforehand. They accrue before the fact rather than as belabored separate actions later.

By lessening competition of products for street space, product density is reduced. By reducing stimuli competing for man's attention, urban chaos is lessened. Although Mies van der Rohe's dictum "Less is more" applies, the resultant cityscape need not be visually sparse or "Miesianlooking" unless the designer wishes it so. Very likely the application of one plus one equals three will yield a completely new visual third dimension which will be an exciting quality in the urban cityscape.

Part Two

Man

Chapter Four

Consumer Is King

Meeting the environmental needs of man is the purpose of urban design; furnishing and equipping the city in the way people want is what this book is about. In a democratic society this should mean the seeking of the greatest good for the greatest number, rather than conferring a private vision on a selected few. However, as soon as we try to create the environment of universal appeal, we realize little is known about the most basic questions of all: What do people want from their surroundings? How are they affected by their environment?

If man is proposed as the all-important factor in the environmental man-machine systems equation, an understanding of his unique sensory capabilities and limitations is required.

The thoughtful designer has always worked along the lines of the social and behavioral scientist. He is sensitized to human feeling and behavior, and he uses a precise procession of procedures to order the environment so as to appeal to the human senses of hearing and smell as well as sight. Clearly, systems development can only be made effective by applying psychological principles.

They Aren't Buying That Brand Anymore

A close relationship between client and designer during programming and design development helps ensure acceptability of the end product. But who is the client? In the design of the public right-of-way and its equipments the ultimate relationships are not always clearly evident. For although the line of contractual responsibility stretches between designer and bureaucracy, final approval rests not only with government but also with the business community and/or the public at large. And as consumers, the public will base acceptance on criteria of the marketplace rather than technical factors —cost of maintenance, for example. Therefore the need for great visual appeal and user satisfaction should be specified in the systems goals and evaluation criteria at the outset.

Presently, products in the public space seldom offer security, comfort, status, pleasure—the most elementary agreeable sensations that contribute to a good life. The term "street improvements" usually means structural, legal, or financial alterations or additions. Rarely does it mean betterment of emotional or social conditions.

Because of lack of progress in areas of significance, people reject their cities. The individual's refusal to buy the product is demonstrated countless times a day by his actions (or avoidance of action).

Examples: Talented or dynamic people leave a city for lack of interesting activities as much as for lack of economic opportunity. Middle-class employees refuse to work in the slums, so business moves to the suburbs. Businessmen reject a potential plant site because of a poor impression received at an inadequate airport terminal. Parents take children on a college shopping tour and choose the most attractive campus. Shoppers drive past dowdy neighborhood plazas to a far-off enclosed shopping center.

This consumer selectivity is accelerating today because our more affluent population has less community identification and more mobility. The grass is greener somewhere else even if it is synthetic, and fewer people, young or old, are locked into position. People are shifting from one end of the continent to the other seeking what they want where they think it is.

But the intent here is not to dwell on these well-known facts; rather, it is to emphasize the universal competitive effects. Every community, unless it is to lose the flow of profits and power, must compete with every other community for jobs from industry, school support from the state, and more money to rebuild with from the federal government.

This competition can be beneficial to the public if as a consequence city agencies offer a product of greater value. City administrators *can* assign greater priority to human needs relative to purely technical considerations in evaluating future community facilities, and a few are already doing just this thing. For example, in computerizing the capital-improvement system for the Wichita, Kansas portion of the 1966 RAA demonstration grant mentioned earlier, priority determinants were established for each possible project. Many possible public works programs were competing for available funds, and selection criteria were required. Noteworthy is the realistic appraisal of major factors in the decision-making process, with assigned weights reflecting their relative importance:

Factor	Weight
Citizen desires	4
Protection of life and property	2
Community promotion	2
Traffic movement	1
Drainage improvement	1

Certainly there can be little doubt that the administrator who satisfies citizen desires will have popular support for the execution of a project, and the people have power. But they have little knowledge and are not organized so as to have a decision-making capability or authority. Therefore the designer needs to serve the administrator in the useful role of people-oriented problem solver. He must be evaluator as much as anything else, researching the needs of the community.

The designer must also analyze the market needs and synthesize these human wants into design concepts which can be produced by industry with economy through the mass-production process. He will achieve his greatest success in improving the urban environment by paying attention to the ordinary details of daily life.

Criteria for Consumer Appeal

Presently we are in a period of great social change; never before have we had change at today's pace. Consider the increase in knowledge. It is said that the first doubling of knowledge since the birth of Christ took place about 1750, the second doubling in 1900, the third about 1950, and the fourth only ten years later in 1960. This means that daring as the most innovative physical change in the public environment may seem today, it is predictable that in a few years improved technology will permit far more revolutionary ones.

Technological change is highly desirable. We should admit that our cities grew by happenstance, without plan or order, in a frantic rush to meet the commercial and residential demand as rural America exploded into a mighty manufacturing nation. But these facilities cannot serve the changed needs of this half of the century. A replacement program is required. And the replacements themselves should not be considered inviolate or sacrosanct.

Yet many prominent figures still say the most important feature of an urban atmosphere should be "enduring values." This raises questions like "What and whose values?" The term "enduring" is seldom defined, and its worth young people constantly question. Nonetheless, as with corporate identity, change in order to improve community identity does not require rejection of continuity. Connection to the past and a sense of perspective sharpen our sensibility when we set out to approve or reject the new. Change must be purposeful, with new values substituted only when shown to be superior to the old. We now know that through conservation and heritage the city can be made more meaningful. The bulldozer blitz of the cityscape has been thoroughly discredited.

But the professional does not accept existing features or established criteria and concepts simply because they are there. To do so delimits creative scope and positions the designer behind the consumer, who subconsciously performs a dynamic evaluation. This questioning of society's values by the public transcends the usual alienation of younger generation from older. At this time in the history of cities a disaffection with the environment exists among most age groups, as well as racial and economic strata. The very young and the blacks may be more perceptive, and impatient, and their reflexes may be quicker, but in any event in much of society there is a growing attack on values based on materialism which results in "things." This has been expressed by Robert C. Wood as the "growing disinclination among the less powerful, the poor and the young, for example, to accept passively the judgements of those accustomed to running things."

What are the most valid criteria for consumer appeal in this dynamic social context?

Change of some unique, outstanding, and favorable kind should be a deliberate part of the process of making one particular place differ from every other dot on the dot-studded map.

Disposability offers far greater design possibilities in changing to immaterialism than does adherence to enduring values. For today the value of an object is not in the object, but in how people think about it. Mass-produced products are seldom considered valuable things anymore. In the public environment this means quality can be achieved by products being common and available, not exclusive and restricted. When common things are expendable, then planners can more freely use the medium of change. Disposability permits industry to improve the standard of city living through techniques similar to those employed in furnishing the home with synthetic products a generation ago. Then the housewife knew she was receiving little utility or gratification from a coal-burning stove, laundry hand-wringer, or

"Be-in," Buffalo, New York.

Washington, D. C. The ghetto consumer rejects the product (environment).

gramophone. Little persuasion was required to induce her to discard obsolescent appliances for the readily apparent benefits of cooktop, washer-drier, and self-wound record player. Given the choice and shown articles of new technology promoting greater comfort and amenity, the city dweller will not hesitate to approve junking of antiquated public facilities.

Mass production of components is essential to the goal of providing a better public environment for an expanding population. The transformation of our cities within tolerable economic limits can only be achieved by means of the massive resources and production capability of industry. Therefore the unlimited possibilities inherent in serial production processes must immediately replace handcraft and building-trades practices as the source for design concepts.

This does not mean that quantification is the goal in itself or that a decline in quality need result. In fact, new products yet to come in surveillance, sensing, lighting, and control will be made possible by the rigorous quality standards, sophisticated tooling, and precision capability of the industrial process. Because of both quantity and quality, industry will inevitably assume a more dominant role in shaping our environment than at present. And here designers can be useful. An overview of community goals must be maintained. The designer can be instrumental in relating industrial capability to user needs. But he can do this only if he couches his creations in machine language.

Miniaturization means *minimal* design. The fewer intrusions into our urban living space, by housekeeping items, the better. In the private sector, outhouses and exposed plumbing are symbols of inadequate sanitary facilities and poverty, and few people tolerate them. In the public sector, telephone and utility wires dangling from wooden poles, once a symbol of municipal affluence, now advertise urban poverty and cannot any longer be accepted. Primitive facilities of gross size must be removed. In the process of furnishing the city anew, the design direction should be size reduction and/or concealment of urban utilities and hardware.

Bigger is not necessarily better. A more effective systems relationship can be achieved through more appropriate scaling of components to each other and to the environment. Product proliferation requires us to reduce component size and conserve space. Every product can be redesigned by this criterion. Lighting transformers can be reduced in bulk or buried in vaults; fire hydrants can be put beneath the floor or relocated to the building fascia; traffic information can be more effectively displayed by means of electronic message-generating media than sign letter forms; traffic-control apparatus can be minimized through solid-state design.

Products of minimal design are not yet available from catalogs. The proportions and size of present-day street furniture are not based on human measurements or capabilities. Even for neighborhood use all available prod-

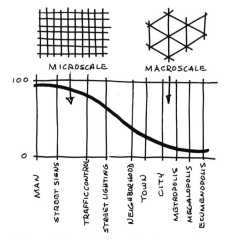

Design relationship of man, furniture, and environment.

ucts are scaled to automobile size and speed. Admittedly, the expressway or corridor is an environment unto itself. There man travels like a space voyager cocooned in a steel and plastic capsule and sealed from contact with earthly things. But in the pedestrian environment of neighborhood, campus, and shopping center, community furnishings of new design are required to stimulate a sense of contact, involvement, and personal relationships.

In order to achieve components of minimal dimension, it is necessary to shift to consumer scale. The point of view of the traditional architect has been omniscient, from on high, grandiose, productive of monumental squares and plazas. The future needs of the megalopolises may result in megastructures that dwarf man. But today's designer needs to see the city from the viewpoint of the man in the street—eyeball height, 5 feet 6 inches from the floor—and to think small.

Imagery of wide consumer appeal is essential if a community is to retain the support of the populace and attract favorable attention. Such imagery can be inherent in the natural environment in features of climate or terrain that are striking and unique. But few cities are so blessed, fewer grasp the nature of the blessing, and almost none reinforce natural wonders or capitalize them by upgrading the surrounding urban areas. Niagara Falls, New York, for example, has been slow to remove the shoddy stores and blight surrounding America's greatest natural attraction. The fact is, however, that imagery need not be based on a natural wonder. In a synthetic age identity can be man-made and can be more precisely made. Ideas are what distinguish one community from another. If the objective of imagery is to appeal to the observer's emotions, then the generation of community design parameters must revolve about consumer preferences. The possibilities are limitless. And the variety of imaginative proposals that have found favor in the past is astounding.

Abroad, notable community identity has been achieved by crowd-pleasing cathedrals, gardens, plazas, funiculars, amusement parks—all the various public places that induce active consumer involvement. Their success has erroneously been interpreted in the United States as calling for efforts to achieve a traditional appearance here. The result has been an aping of style mannerisms described as "classical." At the time of the city-beautiful era, designers could succeed with this approach, as in the Charles River development at Boston. But now it is no longer acceptable or desirable for the serious designer to polish the patina of tradition, even though the means exist for the mass production of "instant tradition": witness the rapidity with which new slums emblazoned YE OLDE VILLAGE are built, or the overnight appearance of ubiquitous gas lanterns for gasoline stations as symbols of beautification.

Two mother lodes rich in the stuff of environmental design can be mined for raw materials of intrinsic worth. The first area of design resources is the American idiom of showmanship and merchandising, that agreeable and exciting exaggeration of scale that sells something.

This quality of urban dynamics is missing in most depersonalized corporate and public construction projects. The environmental designer can restore or sharpen a sense of involvement and concern by utilizing combinations of materials, lighting, and color in variations of scale that touch and move the observer. The road to romance and adventure is lined with banners waving, bands playing, and lights splashing across the sky.

The second source of design concepts lies in the manifestations of our technological age to which the younger consumer best relates. As McLuhan points out, the message is in the media; and the media of kinesthetic sculpture and luminal art convey a more timely message than Grecian columns and Victorian lanterns. The systems designer, unfettered by past precedent, is free to create imagery of new dimensions by evolving new components and relationships to satisfy system performance criteria. A new design vocabulary is being developed featuring the plug-in, add-a-part, discard-a-part processes of the computer age.

These contemporary solutions will be useful solutions and not contrived, just as the San Francisco cable car was a working solution to the transportation needs of the mechanical age contrived with flair and daring in mechanical-age terms. A comparable creation was the Eiffel Tower, an innovative product of late-nineteenth-century technology which we still recognize to be valid and useful. However, what other cities need to express this age are obviously not more cable cars and towers of ironmongery, but transportation modes and street furniture of utility whose expressiveness will produce popular appeal and acquire a renown of their own.

Space to move in is a vital need for the city dweller. With 80 percent of the nation's population soon living on 1 percent of the land, a pileup of people is taking place. The time seems to be coming when a person moving 2 feet in either direction will bump into someone or something.

Many signs and signals are competing for attention, yet when viewed comprehensively, they produce more visual congestion than signal. The human organism has had to adapt to these contaminants polluting visual space as well as the more readily evident hazards of air and water pollution. The problem becomes apparent when one considers the brain as an enormously complex instrument that classifies and interprets all the sense data an individual is exposed to. The brain apparently has a filtering system in the feedback loop that stops transmission of many of the stimuli. But too much gets through, the social scientists are telling us. The observer is subject to communication overload and responds by withdrawal, by ignoring even the essential messages. It becomes a vital question of safety. As Lewis

American Folk Art. Squaw and papoose.

Expo 67, Montreal.

Ghirardelli Square, San Francisco.

The new design vocabulary.

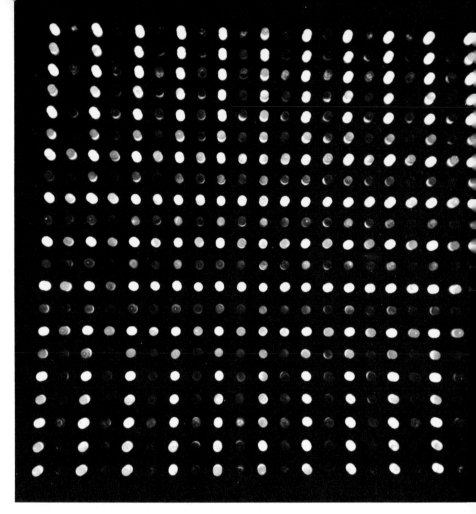

Form-making process which meets the variable environmental needs of man.

Mumford said, "We are overwhelmed by our symbol-creating capacity. [In order to survive] we have learned to achieve a certain opacity, a thickening of the hide."

Another critical problem which the environmental designer must face is the increasingly aggressive behavior of man. As the population increases, so does interpersonal aggression. An aggression explosion chain-reacts from the population explosion. Therefore increasing attention has been devoted to the man-environment relationship so that the urban designer can help defuse an aggression explosion. According to microbiologist Rene Dubos, "an impoverished environment results almost inevitably in biological and mental deficiency." Research indicates space is a determinate variable in man's behavior. Spatial settings trigger responses so deeply hidden that the individual is not even consciously aware of them. When space is inadequate, stress is built up, making possible disruptive and even lethal effects.

"Density" is a word often used in discussions of crowding. But "density" is no longer adequate to describe what is happening to great numbers of people living in overcrowded cities. "Intensity" best describes what faces the urban-pressure-cooker dweller struggling to reach home, office, or food market. Intensity, caused not only by congestion of human bodies but also by the accumulation of "foreign" bodies, by the clutter found in crowded streets and shopping-plaza parking lots, finally gets to people, creating a sense of hostile space.

Research is now establishing human levels of tolerance for crowding, visual congestion, noise, odors, and other sensory factors. Spatial arrangements that can complement man's needs vary from culture to culture. The problem facing us in rebuilding and equipping our cities is understanding the needs of large numbers of people. Particularly people in slums. It is less useful to measure the land-density needs of an affluent suburban commuter. His spatial experience is extended by travel and vacations. What of the ghetto dweller who has no place to go to recharge his senses and who needs a safety valve?

The environmental designer does not plan social actions, but he can provide man the refreshment he needs on the city streets.

MEASURING MAN

Why should anyone but a psychologist or physiologist want to know how we perceive the environment? The question has especial validity, since many concerned with improving the environment still believe science to be incompatable with imagination. The answer lies in the fact that designers are traditionally preoccupied with visual patterns of structures—what one sees. They think, design, and render in a manner that is primarily visual. But the environmental experience is a multisensory one, and designers have to design to exploit man's multisensory capabilities. Above all, for the designer the human material is the most interesting of all. The sensorial equipment of man includes visual, auditory, and other sense receptors, and today he is surrounded by a crowded, demanding world. Sounds, lights, and other attention-seeking stimuli constantly bombard the consumer. We know that people are more sensitive to, and react more strongly to, certain ones (light waves). Why and how the consumer discriminates one from the other is important. As designers, we are continually tickling these senses.

Consider the visual modality. Too much is demanded of our eyes when driving. It is estimated that 80 percent of all impressions are received through the eyes. It is not desirable or necessary to send all information through one sensory system. However, the American way of life encourages this phenomenon. There is picture talk all around us. We are visual. People respond to pictures, not talk.

SOCIOPETAL SPACE (alien to man)

SOCIOFUGAL SPACE (suitable to man)

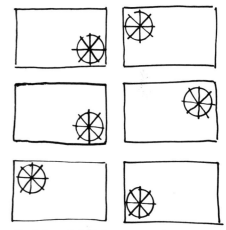

Psychology of spatial arrangements.

Almost everyone is familiar with the description of the eye as an instrument for measurement. This organ measures light by means of sensitive cell structures called rods and cones. These visual cells are of two types comparable to fast and slow film. The rods mediate vision in starlight, like fast film. The slower cones activate at an illumination level one thousand times greater than the rods. There are considerably fewer cones than rods, and they are all packed together in the fovea, which is the center of the retina.

The designer of visual systems such as communications, traffic control, and lighting should consider the extent to which these receptors determine visual acuity. This human ability to distinguish fine detail depends upon this physical structure. Urban product systems that require levels of sensory discrimination exceeding this ability are dangerous. Example: lighting patterns at superhighway interchanges that appear confusing during night driving. To achieve more effective system performance, the designer might help increase observer visual acuity by:

1. Sharpening contrast between object and background
2. Providing greater nighttime light intensity

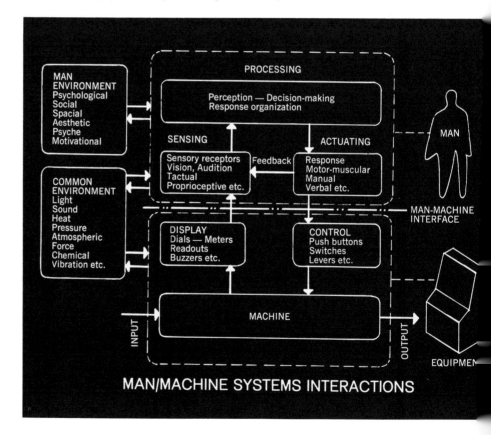

MAN/MACHINE SYSTEMS INTERACTIONS

Hazardous roadway lighting, the result of disregard for user needs and capabilities.

3. Arranging for more observance time

4. Simplifying display

Visual acuity, moreover, decreases with the distance of the object from the eye and with the angle of retinal stimulation. The eye does not see well at angles other than perpendicular to the fovea. An object only 20 degrees off center can be acquired by the fovea only one-tenth as well as an object that is straight ahead. This should influence the siting of various components. Obviously it is physiologically impossible to look straight ahead while driving and simultaneously read a sign mounted at the side of the road or on a building wall.

Seeing Is Believing

The psychology of perception is concerned with the organization and arrangement of complex forms of stimulation. One of the most vital psychological phenomena is the ability of the human being to perceive a world of three dimensions: height, width, and depth. Man can even achieve visual space perception generated by images on a two-dimensional surface.

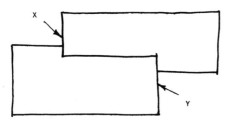

Interposition: the relative position (in space) of the two rectangles changes as vision shifts from X to Y.

Principle of similarity.

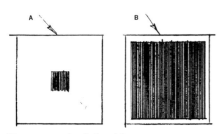

Figure-ground relationship.

The retina has but two dimensions. There is no depth. The retinal image of one object can only be to the left or right of, and/or above or below, the retinal image of another object. How the consumer records, interprets, and organizes these constantly shifting light patterns on the retina affects what he sees. Perception of three-dimensional space is initiated by two different sets of cues: environmental cues and physiological mechanisms, such as visual receptors. The designer is interested mainly in the manipulation of environmental cues for greater sensory gratification.

Environmental, or stimulus, cues initiate or reinforce three-dimensional perception. Some of the principal modes by which we perceive space and objects are:

Linear perspective
Light and shadow
Clearness (near objects defined, far objects hazy)
Movement (near objects faster)
Gradient (texture flattened with distance)
Interposition

Interposition can be especially useful to the product designer in creating depth and solidity or in giving special emphasis to certain features of the product. How the observer spontaneously perceives the figure is of critical importance to the designer, as in the matter of framing buildings or products.

Perceptual organization usually relates behavior to complex patterns of stimuli rather than an individual stimulus element. This "principle of similarity" is observed in the adjacent-stimulus pattern of twenty-five symbols, where the observer tends to perceive the pattern as a ground of columns, not rows of space. This is a function of how he sees *things,* not the spaces between. This is important to the designer evaluating a product in the environment, since like objects tend to be perceived together and, conversely, unlike objects appear separate. When shapes are constructed, the square will appear more like any other square than a circle. If a designer's primary concern were to create an attention-getting unique identity for a fire-alarm box in a sequence of other square shapes, he might differentiate by making it round.

There are many of these kinds of gestalt perceptual organizations. One of the best known is the "figure-ground relationship," in which perceptions vary so that a shape silhouetted in the foreground may alternately be seen as background. In the example, each shape may be seen as a hole or as a thing on a surround.

Illusions are false perceptions. The perceptual process organizes physical stimulation. Sometimes it organizes erroneously. When the designer permits this to happen, the physical environment is perceived in a way that does not correspond to reality. There are innumerable examples, only a few of which are mentioned.

Illusions of shape occur frequently. In the example shown the square is distorted due to its relationship to the circle. This poses obvious architectural and product design implications.

Illusions of size can be useful or harmful to design, as in the famous Müller-Lyer illusion, in which both vertical lines are equal in length but not perceived as such.

Illusions of brightness are achieved by strong contrast between figure and ground. A dark line or spot will appear darker in general as the brightness of its environment is increased; conversely, a white spot surrounded by a dark environment will appear brighter as the latter is darkened. In other words, black and white juxtaposed reinforce each other. The importance of contrasts in brightness or in color cannot be overemphasized; many practical demonstrations are visible at night under various light conditions. White traffic markings, for example, appear whiter on black asphalt than on concrete.

Illusions of movement are typified by the psychotechnical consideration know as "Phi phenomenon," an apparent movement where in fact none occurs. This is the design basis for many of those flashing, moving arrows that advertise the presence of roadside businesses. They are meant to be obviously, violently garish. They are, in fact, irresistible as attention getters.

These stationary signs that appear to move are successful because the designer has utilized a 1912 discovery of Max Wertheimer, founder of the

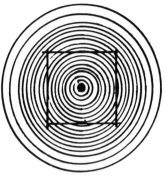

Illusion of shape.

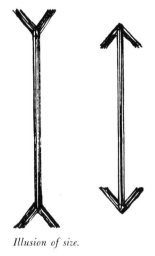

Illusion of size.

Two equal gray patterns which appear lighter or darker depending on background.

Concentric circles behind convex plastic lens. Observer himself becomes kinetic element by looking into lens and creating movement effect when in fact none exists.

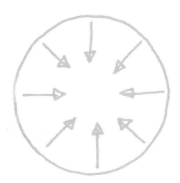

gestalt school of psychology. Wertheimer projected two short parallel lines, 1 centimeter apart, at reading distance from the subject. The lines were flashed on a screen one after the other. The length of the time interval between the successive flashes determined what the subject perceived. When the interval between the exposure of each line was longer than 0.03 seconds, the subject perceived only what actually existed: two stationary lines, first one and then the other. When the interval was shorter than 0.002 seconds, the two lines appeared to be projected simultaneously. When the time interval was from 0.03 to 0.002 seconds, the observer perceived a flashing movement, with the first line seeming to jump from its own position to the second position.

The psychology of perception is being stressed because the designer should recognize that perception is synthetic rather than analytic. Man tends to put things together in wholes. This is perhaps most evident in reading, where we perceive shapes in words and phrases rather than individual letters. But while the basic quality of perception is the relating of one thing to another, any form of design language or coding depends upon distinguishing one thing from another. A thing usually carries information and is meaningful only to the degree that it is separable.

An awareness of the synthesizing nature of perception will help the designer achieve urban equipment solutions within the psychological capabilities of man. Simplicity of product design through invoking more effective modes of controlling human behavior will have to come because of the increased demands made on the psychological and physiological apparatus of perception. Indeed, the safety of the streets may depend upon the extent to which the designer utilizes available data on human sensory capabilities.

Thus psychological consideration of the consumer is necessary in all typical environmental system development activities such as:

Establishing the design problem
Determining the systems package that will meet human needs
Establishing relationships between man and machines
Designing the product environment
Installing the systems and evaluating them in terms of human usage
Previously it was suggested that scaling the forms of the street furniture to fit man and make him comfortable enhances consumer appeal in that people can touch and feel, enjoy or ignore, as they choose. But clearly it is not good enough to be merely functional or even handsome. Furnishing the city requires meeting psychological and social needs.

Part Three

Environment

Chapter Five

Shaping the City Floor

Certainly most basic to the socioeconomic life of the urban environment are appropriate roads and streets and public places. In any but the most narrow definition, the creation of an acceptable public environment must include many considerations beyond paving materials.

No longer can cities install or repave streets using codes and criteria of minimum performance as the purchasing specification. To compete with the suburbs, as well as to meet the needs of urban developers and neighborhood residents, each with specific wants, the bureaucracy must plan and rebuild according to design standards of maximum performance that provide consumer satisfaction, comfort, and pleasure, as well as according to engineering considerations of maintainability and efficiency.

How will this be done? How will Downtown and the neighborhood street be restored to the people as places for enjoyable experiences? The first step is reevaluation of the function of the street in terms of contemporary social goals and economic pressures. Only then can the full resources of industry be applied and the benefits of the multidisciplinary approach to design be achieved.

PEOPLE ON WHEELS

Establishing Goals and Priorities

The street has always performed a number of communal functions. More than a way of movement, it has been a space for human activity—buying and selling, socializing, providing visual orientation to the visitor, symbolizing community character. Above all, through history, the street has been the road to romance.

A thousand years ago the Mayan trod the sacred sacebob of crushed white limestone threading through cedar and mahogany. Fragrant plants bloomed while brilliantly plumaged birds swooped and chattered. Ahead appeared the plazas, their platforms and pyramids white against the green lianas and palms. The Mayan became emotionally involved. He had reason to support this city and contribute to its splendor. He received from it benefits that contributed to his well-being and pride of association.

Little more than a hundred years ago the western settler rode horse and wagon through vast dry spaces until he reached the dusty track leading into the frontier town. Ahead he saw wooden sidewalks above the muddy manure-covered road. His spurs jangled when he strode the springy boards. False fronts and large signs promised full meals and drink. Main Street was a package whose delights were clearly defined to the traveler by sight, smell, and sound.

Then the auto roared into town, and the pedestrian experience has never been the same. The American Downtown has become dull and boring. Neighborhood streets have evolved into a place to drive through to get someplace else. Automobile movement has suppressed all other functions. Millions of miles of standardized black asphalt and hundreds of thousands of uniform traffic signs have obliterated the visual cues to where you are and where you've been.

It has been estimated that with the advent of expressways and belt loops *two-thirds* of downtown land has been given to moving and storing automobiles! Compare the area devoted to public right-of-way (not counting off-street parking) with that available for all other possible uses in the following typical urban renewal projects:

Example: Louisville, Kentucky, West Downtown

Total acres	290.0
Streets, alleys, etc.	99.0

Example: Buffalo, New York, Waterfront

Total acres	292.8
Streets, alleys, etc.	104.2

Pedestrian bridge erected across Broadway at Fulton, New York City, 1867. Removed 1868 because consumers preferred traffic hazards to climbing stairs.

Example: San Francisco, California, Western Addition

Total Area	276.0
Streets, Alleys, etc.	107.0

These and similar statistics suggest not only the possibility of wasteful overdesign as a general practice but also the opportunities at hand by virtue of public ownership for more efficient use of the vast amounts of expensive urban land.

Detailed discussion of transportation planning and land-use criteria is not within the scope of this book. But it must be noted that the shape of the urban fabric results from the selection of route and mode of circulation and the integration of transportation systems.

As Ian McHarg has pointed out in *Landscape Architecture,* qualitative factors are now considered only *after* the conclusion of cost/benefit analysis.

Present procedure by federal and state agencies involves calculating savings from, and costs of, the proposed urban highway. Savings are computed in time, operating costs, and reduction of accidents. Costs are those of construction and maintenance. Savings must exceed costs by a factor of 1 to 1.2.

This formula is no longer adequate. Future projects should from the outset be programmed to include social benefits as well as physiographic and traffic-engineering criteria. More emphasis should be placed on designs that favor least loss of taxable land. A formula based on least social cost and maximum social benefit will result in maximum social utility.

This poses difficulties. Novel considerations are interjected into the cost/benefit formula (though present methods of highway engineering allocate money values to convenience, a commodity as difficult to quantify as esthetics). Moreover, evaluation of new proposals must always be in terms relevant to contemporary goals. Everyone says we are going to rebuild America in the next thirty years. It will be the same old piece of merchandise unless we develop a new physical expression derived from a change in technology that satisfies goals of improved efficiency, added safety, greater public comfort, and less destruction of the urban fabric.

SEPARATING WHEELS FROM PEOPLE

Three-dimensional Design

One of the most critical urban design problems is the increasing transformation of city street into corridor or limited-access highway. Each city has its examples. In Chicago the Pershing Road Corridor will cut back private property along the roadway and expand from 66 feet to 150 feet in width. Many city comprehensive plans anticipate that major streets will have variable standards of width and other characteristics, depending upon traffic volume and the nature of the areas through which they pass. Where previous linear-city proposals utilized utility lines or railroads as the spine, current thinking uses the expressway as the spine. Such plans also suggest that multidisciplinary design be done by a task force whose members are drawn from the design professions as well as highway engineering. In practice, however, this seldom effectively happens.

Jane Jacobs's reaction was to write, "Most cities widen roadbeds. Far better to widen sidewalks." Perhaps other alternatives exist. In order to more efficiently separate incompatible traffic—pedestrian, auto, truck, mass transit—cities could be redesigned utilizing available air rights as well as the surface and subsurface. Many older solutions still apply as well as newer techniques. Their viability has been proved. The engineering know-how exists.

We could look to the New York or the Chicago "el" as a proved way

Midtown Plaza, Rochester, New York. Proto-type protected mall is surrounded by stores, offices, hotel; there is even parking below and natural daylight above.

to increase the carrying capacity of existing streets. Subways are another example; those of Montreal are a particularly pleasant public experience. Monorails are back in vogue. We could note how the UN Park sits on a platform cantilevered over the East River Drive to create usable space where none existed before. We see the trend to put public parking underground in cities with hills such as San Francisco (Union Square) or Pittsburgh (Mellon Park). Something besides a park can be put on top of the parking. On a campus it might be tennis courts; downtown it might be a shopping plaza and hotel, such as Victor Gruen's Midtown Plaza in Rochester, New York. Or parking may be underneath the downtown office-building complex, as popularized by Rogers, Taliaferro, Kostritsky and Lamb at Charles Center, Baltimore, and Fountain Square, Cincinnati. Now even sports stadiums are elevated with parking under the podia, so direct enclosed access is provided from mobile seat to sports seat. In Washington, D.C., Nathaniel Owings was able to make L'Enfant's baroque patte d'oie, or goose-foot intersection, at the foot of Capitol Hill finally work by putting much of the traffic underground.

In the more successful large-scale spatial solutions to roadway congestion or circulation problems, separation has been achieved by use of two or more horizontal planes, one carrier level precisely over another, much as on a double-decker bridge. But a quantum jump will occur when we exploit the full potential of omnidirectional air rights. Then all activities, pedestrian and motorist as well as commercial, can be enhanced through interwoven ar-

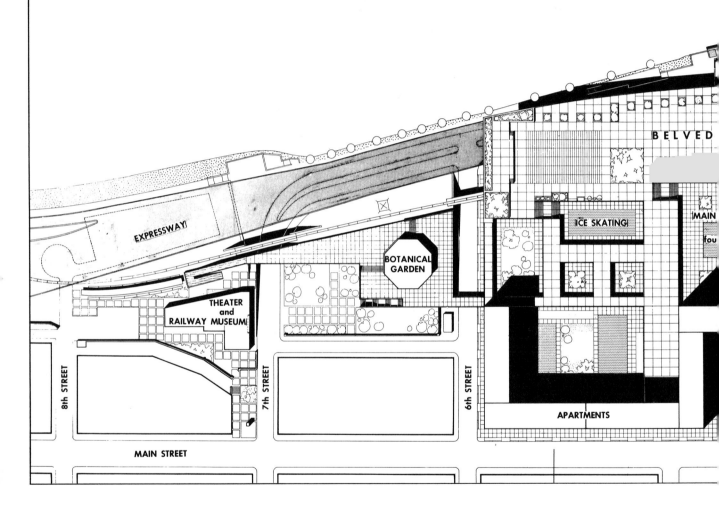

OHIO RIVER

BELVED

EXPRESSWAY

BOTANICAL
GARDEN

ICE SKATING

MAIN

fou

THEATER
and
RAILWAY MUSEUM

APARTMENTS

8th STREET

7th STREET

6th STREET

MAIN STREET

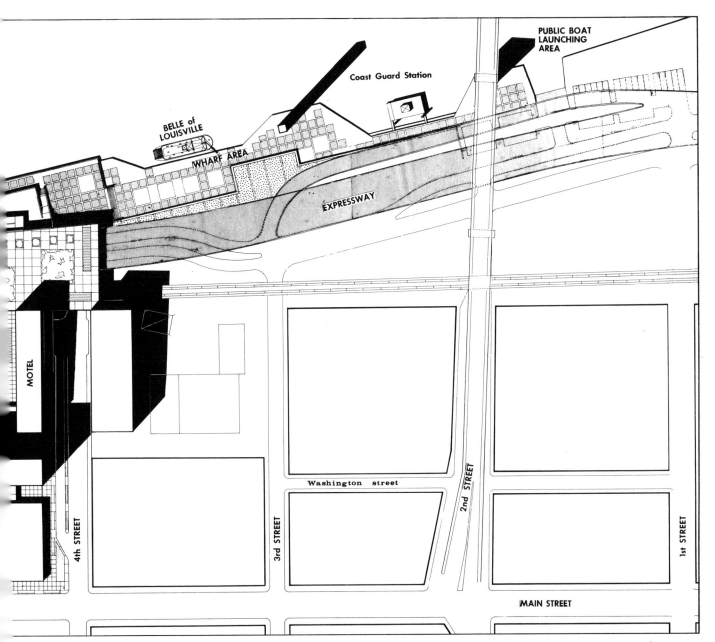

Multilevel development on public land brings new vitality to abandoned Louisville waterfront.

Fountain Square, Cincinnati.

rangements of spaces, uses, and access paths. Existing available public land can become a multidimensional linkage to private spaces.

Some such projects already exist. An elementary but pioneer installation has been made in Morristown, Tennessee. Its 1967 Skymart, believed to be the first double-deck sidewalk in the United States, runs 1,000 feet down each side of Main Street, provides access to second stories of commercial buildings, and carries power and telephone lines, eliminating overhead wires.

A more sophisticated pedestrian passageway is that of Cincinnati, based on a plan by Rogers, Taliaferro, Kostritsky and Lamb. This linkage moves irregularly through much of the downtown core at a 15-foot-high level and connects by spines and spurs many stores, hotels, and garages. This project demonstrates that linkage need not be linear, "hard-edge," or axial in the European tradition, but can be amorphous, encouraging pedestrian movement in appropriate directions. But its major significance lies in the fact that it takes the city as it is and becomes an additional public right-of-way,

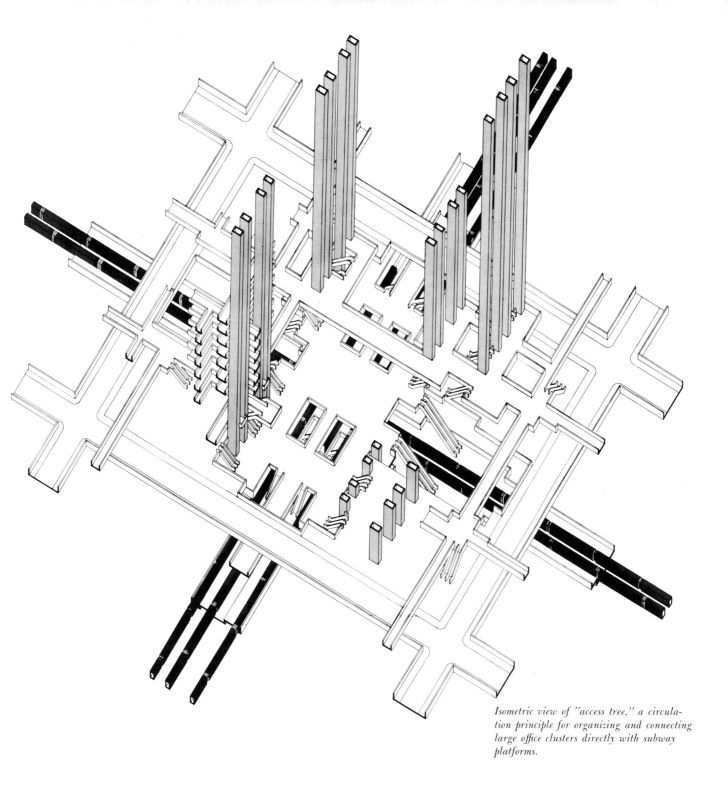

Isometric view of "access tree," a circulation principle for organizing and connecting large office clusters directly with subway platforms.

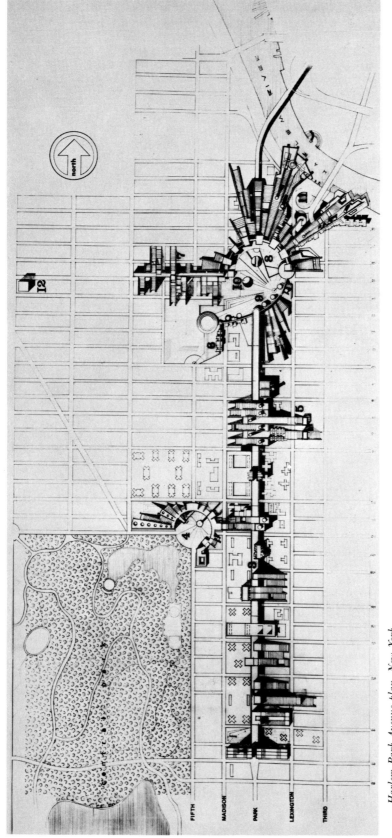
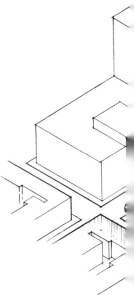

Harlem Park Avenue plan, New York,
1968.

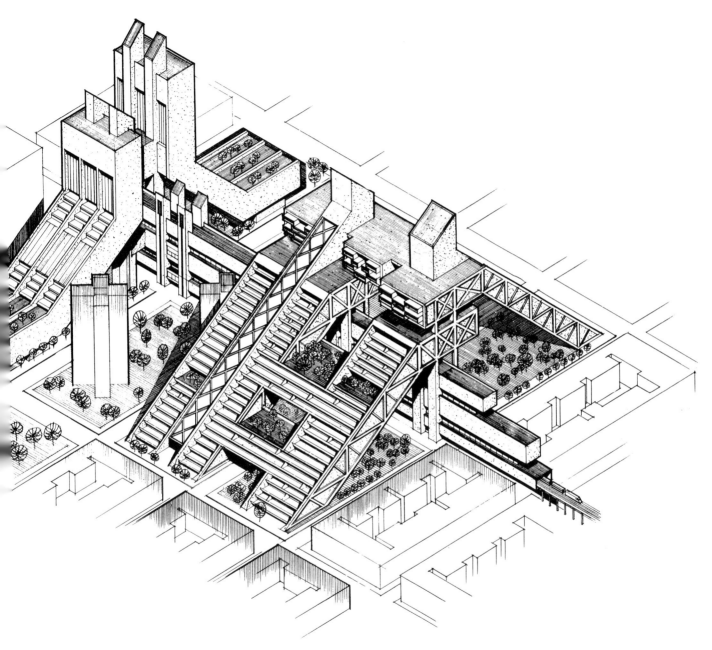

Harlem Park Avenue plan, New York, 1968. Enlarged view showing multilevel use of air rights over Grand Central tracks.

penetrating old as well as new buildings, and only occasionally in register with the streets below.

In the metropolis, the sensibility of the Cincinnati approach is as self-evident to businessmen, developers, and bureaucracy as it is to designers. Since Americans will not give up their love affair with the automobile and in fact want to give it custody of the street, then the pedestrian has to be put above or below the automobile. In the megalopolis, the problems are more intense and the solutions more drastic. Once the people are elevated, the economics suggest, they might as well be transported at the fifteen-story level as at 15 feet. When that happens, the true value of three-dimensional design of public space will be not only separation of wheels from people but people from people.

The success of all these mechanistic concepts will depend not only on the economics of land use but also on whether the proposed transportation system offers people greater enjoyment of the movement experience.

Middle two lanes decoratively converted but seldom used by pedestrians. Predominant street use remains vehicular.

Two-dimensional Design

Meanwhile keeping our two feet on the ground, we need to face immediate problems of separating wheels from people and use the sort of roadway design that still relies on two-dimensional grids: open this street to wheels not people; make this block a mall for people and close it to wheels; make this street an expressway for wheels and close it to people.

Pedestrianism, one mode of transportation which exists in conjunction with all other modes, is nonetheless the most neglected of all modes in current transport analysis and design. Yet walking under proper conditions, is delightful, healthful, and likely to remain important in three areas: in such concentrations as the center city, shopping centers, and campuses, where it is the primary mode of travel; in mode-interchange terminals such as airports; and in the home neighborhood, for school trips, visiting, and local shopping.

Because of their importance to commercial interests, most pedestrian design focus has been placed on malls. These have proliferated throughout America. In its simplest form, a mall can be the identification of a few blocks, usually in an important shopping district, by certain embellishments to the roadway which will attract more shoppers. Very frequently automobile traffic is not restricted from these blocks, because of timidity, cost, or lack of planning. In a more advanced form of mall, the street may be narrowed or configured to hamper vehicles (make them use some other route) or to provide more walking space. Or a large center median may be installed and furnished with decorative lights or plantings.

Sometimes halfway measures only halfway meet expectations. People on wheels will go where they can and not somewhere else. People on foot will not cross dangerous roadways midblock either to shop the other side or to sit on benches in the median in isolated grandeur. Regardless of any superficial appearance of having been inspired by H. G. Wells and Edward Bellamy or the more recent science fiction of movies and TV, the halfway type of urban mall is pale, insipid stuff at best.

An increasingly popular mall design, first developed by Victor Gruen, is one in which existing stores and facilities are not disturbed but wheels are excluded by rerouting. Commonly the street is filled to grade between curbs and enhanced in the central areas to encourage foot traffic and free movement. This design may or may not be successful, depending upon which of two approaches is used in the design treatment of the roadbed.

The unsuccessful approach is that of the hard-edge school of landscape design which evolved from the classic geometry of Beaux-Arts. Decorative linear patterns are used which frequently work at cross-purposes with function. Shopping centers must stimulate spontaneity which encourages com-

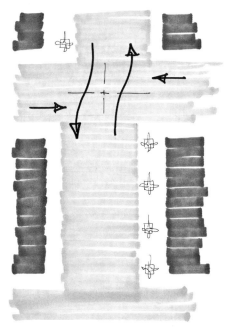

Washington Street Mall, Oakland, California. Pedestrian spaces created by widening alternate sidewalks.

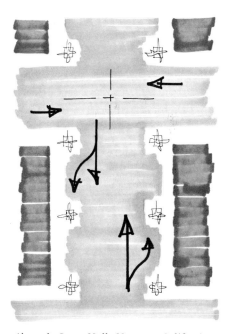

Alvarado Street Mall, Monterey, California. Pedestrian and parking spaces created by widening opposing sidewalks.

*Fresno Mall, California. Conversion of
street to all-pedestrian use. Casual pattern
is conducive to crisscross shopping.*

Prudential Center, Boston.

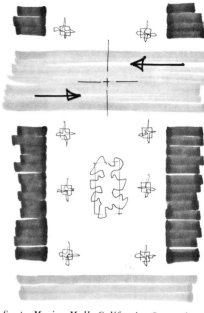

Santa Monica Mall, California. Conversion of street to all-pedestrian use. Formal repetition of sidewalk pattern inhibits crisscross shopping.

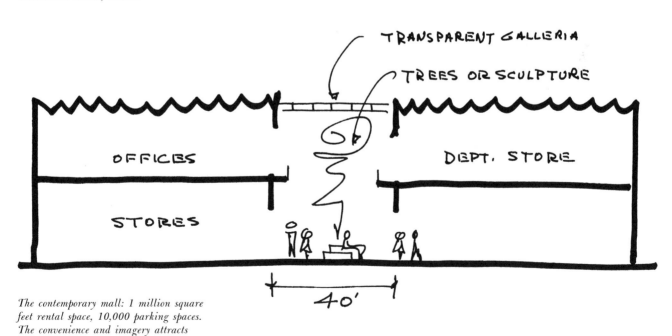

The contemporary mall: 1 million square feet rental space, 10,000 parking spaces. The convenience and imagery attracts 300,000 people.

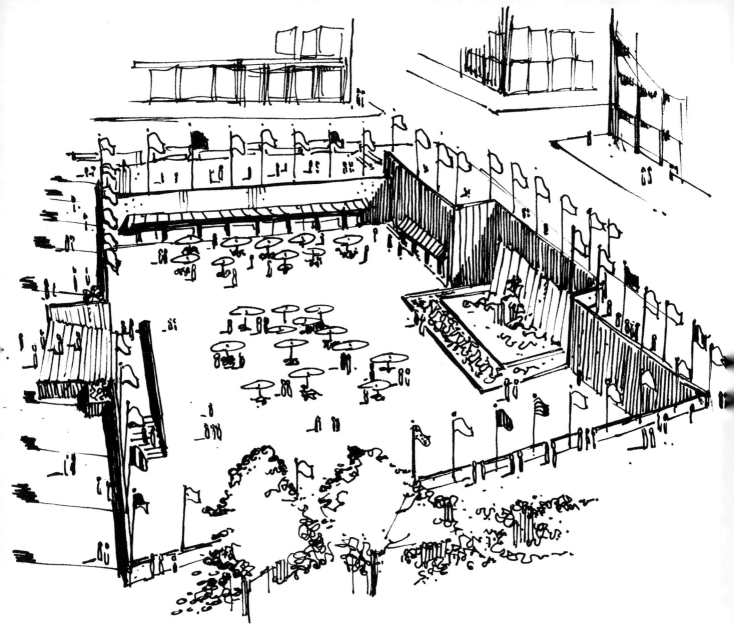

Rockefeller Center, New York.

parison shopping; crossover from side to side is essential. When streets are closed to vehicles and resurfaced as pedestrian malls, the hard-edge approach is to install new paving patterns which conform to the old pedestrian path. The old curbline (now without step) is restated by new decorative patterns that inhibit crossover. In an extreme of architectural vanity, even moats have been used; incredibly filled with water, they obviously perform the age-old function of keeping people away.

Clearly, if we eliminate the need to accommodate automobiles on the roadway, designs more meaningful and relevant than decorative sidewalk patterns can be employed. Developers of the suburban enclosed shopping center have proved that the successful mall is one which denigrates the storefront in relation to the environment and whose public space is made not much more than 40 feet wide to encourage crossover. Because the city right-of-way (storefront to storefront) is usually much wider, it is even more urgent to employ a functional design approach, as typified by several of Victor Gruen's solutions. The essence of this approach is spontaneity rather than Renaissance formality. Store and sight lines are blurred. The middle space is packed with attractions and a focal point; enticing changes in vista are offered to pull people from side to side. The central plaza becomes a place for sunning, sitting, lunching, or watching the girls go by in style.

Perhaps the most important development in the pedestrian space (aside from the enclosed and climate-controlled mall) is the trend to use of multi-level space. Rockefeller Center is usually cited as the early and classic example whose accommodation of varied activities on different levels contributes to an ever-changing vista of interest and excitement. New examples abound of multilevel spaces, such as the shopping promenade under Place Ville Marie in Montreal or L'Enfant Plaza in Washington, both by I. M. Pei.

Place Ville Marie, Montreal.

*Circle Campus of the University of Illinois
at Chicago.*

Of course malls and plazas are built for purposes other than commercial. Take the plaza at the Circle Campus of the University of Illinois at Chicago, which the architects, Skidmore, Owings & Merrill, call a social plaza, a crossroads where young people meet and compare and barter ideas in an intellectual environment. It works in that fashion because it also serves as an elevated pathway, crossing train tracks and continuing at raised level into second-floor building entrances.

But even more plastic pathways will be evolved as a solution to the challenge of confrontation of vehicle and pedestrian. Paved surfaces can be shaped and modeled in swelling shapes whose constantly changing volumes give a sense of excitement and variety to the pedestrian participant.

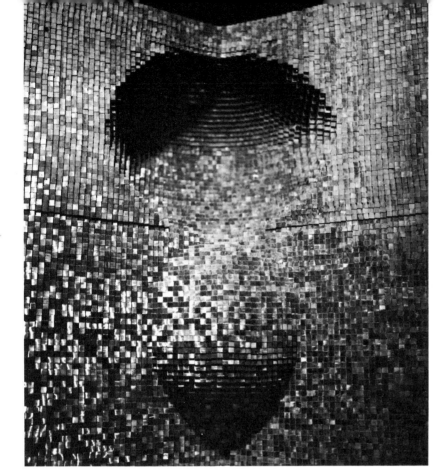

Microscale metal cubes make sculpture and also suggest macroscale future floor.

(Left and above) *Civic Center, San Francisco.*

Auditorium, MIT

INTEGRAL SITE IMPROVEMENTS
Paving

Present practice in new construction or rehabilitation of old streets requires specification and bid by the square yard of paving and by the linear foot of curbing. Lowest first cost prevails, with side effects discounted. Environmental design in terms of human needs or neighborhood social factors is not performed. The potentiality of flooring to convey urbanity, elegance, or distinctive character is unexploited. The design of paving to achieve a neighborhood image has been neglected for the easy and routine, the dull and unimaginative. However, much of today's urban design places emphasis on open space—civic centers, shopping malls, campus podia, office buildings on stilts or utilizing only part of their plot area—and this open space demands increased design consideration of pavement patterns and materials.

Landscape architects traditionally have understood the importance of masonry ground cover as a component in the total design scheme. Texture, color, and pattern have been carefully used to complement the overall scheme harmoniously. Cobblestone, brick, terra-cotta, and asphalt block pavers have all been used with stunning effect. Other designers too have been concerned with the floor and its interface with housekeeping hardware. But the design solution oriented to the Renaissance marble court or church-yard green space is not always responsive to today's needs. What works for the Piazza San Marco doesn't necessarily work elsewhere. Consider what makes the plaza in the new Civic Center of Rochester, New York so stupefyingly dull and forbidding. Is it the lack of pigeons? Or is it the in-applicability of yesterday's materials to today's conditions? Another example is the White House east drive, where the carriageway cobblestones are now partially obscured by a skim coating of black asphalt.

The problems with using traditional elements in traditional patterns are threefold:

1. High product cost (piece production)
2. High installation cost (hand labor)
3. High maintenance cost (chewing-gum removal, salt damage, etc.)
4. High replacement cost (lack of availability of standard units)

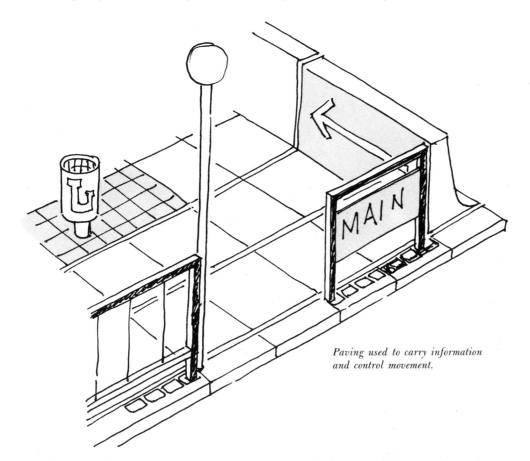

Paving used to carry information and control movement.

In interior design demand spurred industry to a fantastic increase in volume and innovation in resilient, woven, and hard floor coverings; the same can happen in exterior design. Prestige projects may continue to use handmade, hand-laid products. But industry will be required to develop mass-production techniques for new kinds of paving components and materials as designers weave the urban fabric by the mile.

Precast slabs are a beginning, but could be made more useful by greater use of cast-in-place inserts to pre-position and accept other hardware and components such as manholes, lamppost bases, planters, signpost sleeves, drains, etc. Machines could be developed for site use to continuously pour and emboss decorative patterns into concrete or synthetic materials for walks. Old sidewalks and paved surfaces could be rehabilitated by snythetic coatings machine-mixed and -applied.

The floor can be mechanically varied to offer change in reflectivity under artificial light. It can be programmed for sight and sound (visual inserts or add-ons, textural noisemakers) to provide cues and become a continuous information system:

1. To carry traffic or safety markings for motorist or pedestrian

2. To define parking areas

3. To identify "rooms" or special street spaces such as intersections or crossings

4. To provide a sense of territory, marking entrances to neighborhoods or commercial districts

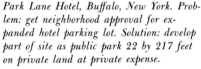

Park Lane Hotel, Buffalo, New York. Problem: get neighborhood approval for expanded hotel parking lot. Solution: develop part of site as public park 22 by 217 feet on private land at private expense.

By performing additional systems tasks, candidate designs offering similar new or additional options will be able to justify initial costs of development.

Barriers

Barriers are for separation. They may limit access and use, but growing complexity and density of spatial use demands better techniques and hardware for channelization and compartmentation. Barriers are sometimes inappropriate or misapplied because the function is not adequately assessed as security from people or safety from vehicles or space delineation. Dr. A. E. Parr has listed three types of barriers: prohibitive (chain-link fences), persuasive (bollards, railings), and suggestive (archways, lighting changes). Evaluation of the problem in broad terms will lead to consideration of many alternatives. Some will not be hardware solutions, but will lead to redesign of other elements to accomplish a dual purpose. Where barriers are essential, they should not be permitted to be stuck to the floor, but should be designed as an essential and integrated component of the urban furnishings.

Fences may serve two completely different functions which are often confused: security and space delineation. As an example of the latter, the genesis of the institution of turf in our cities was the appropriation of a street or housing project by a gang as its own territory. Members of other gangs could not enter without permission of the territory-owning gang. Jane Jacobs has described how this procedure of "fenceless," keeping the other gang out, evolved into middle-class turfs with literal fences to keep the other classes out. Soon high cyclone fences were built around the malls and plazas and playgrounds of developments and projects with signs saying KEEP OUT—NO TRESPASSING.

Now many people live in stockaded villages within a city. Fences are hostile. They are an invitation to attack and will seldom withstand a determined assault. If the function of the fence is to suggest a spatial division, other means such as markings or plantings should be considered.

Bollards are sturdy posts embedded in the floor either to protect some more fragile structure or to exclude vehicles from pedestrian precincts. Although they have an honorable history of traditional use in sculptured form, their use has languished except by highway engineers, who employ steel pipe or sometimes yellow-painted oil drums for the latter purpose.

It would seem, however, that their value in contributing to imagery and in providing an alternative to more formidable or massive constructions has been overlooked. Many materials and shapes can be employed in them which grow from, or integrate well with, floor textures and patterns. Bollards can by position and number act as "punctuation marks" as well as barriers. They can establish sign lines of varying scale and rhythms. They can simplify traffic- or parking-control procedures.

Birmingham University, Staff House, lighting bollards. Precast bollard contains bronze glareless light source. White tile provides reflected sparkle.

"Median" is the engineering nomenclature for a traffic separator, which usually appears as a flat raised curbing in the middle of the road separating opposing vehicles and marking no-man's-land. It's almost always an ugly and dangerous place to be. But thousands of miles of medians in many widths and shapes are poured each year, primarily in major urban roads.

Because of the significance of medians in the cityscape, funds have recently been made available for beautification. But many "beautified" medians are of routine design, with grass or trees at low elevation that are subject to noxious fumes and salt action on soil and plantings and do not provide headlight protection during winter months. Surely here is an opportunity for significant improvement in the public roadway. On-site or prefabricated median segments can be designed in infinite varieties of shape and material to mark *this* road as different from *that*. Shape can convey place, direction, and importance. Shape need not be low and flat, with curbs which require higher and uglier guardrails. The median can be formed of low walls which discourage pedestrians from crossing, mask out approaching headlights at night, and contain linear light sources for flooding the roadway with low-elevation glareless illumination.

WHEELS WITHOUT PEOPLE

The Problem and Goal

When most cities, recreational areas, and other public spaces were established, neither designer nor developer was concerned with the automobile. Existing streets and public transportation were adequate. Monumental buildings required only a carriage entrance; sports stadiums were serviced by trolley tracks. Most people lived near their jobs, frequently above the store or in the mill town. Students used mass transit to get to class; women walked to the neighborhood market. Cars were a luxury, not a necessity. Parking two generations ago was not a problem.

Now the city has exploded with people and pushed out its borders. Society is mobile, and business, shopping, and leisure activities are far-flung and numerous. Walking seems outmoded. Mass transit has lost and not yet regained status. Everyone wants cars and has the affluence to acquire them.

No single feature has so affected the appearance of towns as car parking along streets. The efficiency of streets, their ability to move vehicles and pedestrians, has been drastically reduced by the resulting congestion and disorder. And still there is not enough curb space for all parkers.

The automobile is extremely limited in mobility compared with a pedestrian. It cannot move sideways; it cannot enter restricted spaces. Because of this limited utility it must remain largely in storage. The average car is in motion only 500 hours per year; it is left parked on a paved surface the other 8,260 hours. The average person can stand with an armful of packages in 5 square feet. His whole wardrobe of clothes will take up no more than 2 square feet of closet space. But his car parked on the street will occupy approximately 150 square feet without counting the area required to maneuver him in and out of the resting space.

In simplifying the urban scene the removal of parking spaces with their signs and meters should be given special consideration. Well-organized parking facilities should be provided in accessible places.

Even in suburbia, where shopping-center lots may have a capacity of 8,000 cars, a number which turns over three to four times a day, getting in and out of these shopping-center or off-street lots has become a dangerous adventure. According to the nation's largest traffic insurers, parking-lot damage now appears to be the chief source of minor car claims. People seem to be careless, reckless, and thoughtless. Designers have not created new kinds of facilities that might reduce the consequences. Better layouts could lower the ratio of parking spaces to selling spaces. Better signing and control devices and markings would make more efficient the use of space.

Curb Parking

Curb parking exists because businessmen and the bureaucracy regard it as suitable and sufficient. But nowhere in the urban scene is there more reliance on obsolete procedure and products and less on new ideas, techniques, devices, and signs and markings than in parking control. Moreover, it is expensive. In some middle-size cities the annual cost of parking signs and their installation exceeds $50,000, an amount greater than the cost of street-lighting replacement and maintenance.

More needs to be achieved than token observance of national standards for posting regulations, in themselves confusing and inadequate. Present procedure in the United States is for municipalities to post signs at each location where parking is prohibited. In the center city this practice has gone to the extreme of posting signs every 30 to 50 feet along the curb. Legends are long; typefaces and layout are illegible. Signs with complex schedules of authorized times are admissions of inadequate traffic solutions. The custom in England is to post signs only where parking is permitted. Parking is prohibited by negative information. The need for NO PARKING signs in profusion is deleted.

This procedure could be employed on private parking grounds, where the use of standard highway signs has no legal meaning. *Message sets should be simple, direct, and clear.* It is better to say NO ENTRY than AUTHOR-IZED VEHICLES ONLY. Messages such as SLOW or DRIVE CAREFULLY or CARS TOWED AWAY are of dubious value and should not be used.

Even on the public right-of-way, parking and similar regulatory signs that attempt to cite chapter and verse are futile. Signs should be designed to be explicit and directive, not legalistic.

This informative approach permits development of exciting concepts for communicating parking instructions. Parking areas can be identified with entertaining and memorable symbols, diagrams, or color. Community appearance can be enhanced through use of more pleasing sign panels and lettering materials. The parking authority can be presented as a helpful agency rather than the long arm of the law. By choice of alphabet and sign-panel materials, the identity of a community, urbane or rustic, commercial or residential, can be reemphasized.

Curb parking could also be optimized by greater and more sophisticated use of the floor for conveying messages. Properly used, curbing and paving can tell the driver much about when and how to use the space by means of surface changes and paint. This minimizes the need for sign "things" on poles. Messages or symbols can be set in or applied to the floor. This is not only less costly and more useful but also necessary in certain facilities or areas. While painting of stall lines has become accepted practice along curbs

Church Street Project. Color-coded aluminum parking signs fit in galvanized-steel light standards.

tow zone
no standing
7·9 am
4.30·6pm

no parking
anytime

New Haven Traffic Authority

128

and in off-street parking facilities to define space and lanes, improved use of space and less car damage can be achieved with better-designed band widths and graphics and better placement.

Curb parking is frequently controlled on a time basis as the fair way to utilize space throughout the day. Parking meters, when accompanied by adequate-length stalls and timer restrictions appropriate to demand, may produce the following benefits:

1. Make a set number of spaces available for more parkers by encouraging a more rapid turnover.

2. Simplify enforcement and reduce police personnel required.

3. Liquidate their own cost.

However, these objectives are not always obtained with mechanical control aids. People need spaces for relatively long periods and find it more convenient to feed the device than find a space elsewhere. Frequently they will not use the meters or will resent paying for the "privilege" of parking in order to patronize a store or library or visit a campus. Enforcement requires expensive manpower.

There are a number of variables in meter-head selection, method of support, and siting that may produce either a pleasing installation or a visual disaster. Mechanically, industry classifies meters in two types, manual and automatic. The manual mechanism is wound by the user each time he inserts a coin and turns the handle. The automatic must be periodically wound by the coin collector.

Many of these products are difficult to operate, hard to read, and frequently malfunctional. Coin-operated meters freeze and jam. Many are expressly designed to be unreadable (unexpired time) by the space-seeking motorist in order to secure a higher payoff for the house. The general level of engineering and reliability is of such low order that few of the industry's products are currently useful. In 1966 the city of Buffalo had 3,166 parking meters; they needed maintenance attention in 16,347 instances. Such functional deficiencies make essential the design of new units that meet higher standards.

Perhaps a more fundamental consideration is the manner of installation of the devices. It seems wasteful to use a separate post for each meter for each car. Yet by far the greatest number of installations along curbs and in parking lots are made in this manner. Some have even an additional post embedded in the floor to protect the meter post! Clearly capital cost, maintenance cost, and visual pollution will be reduced by the sharing of one post by two units; even further savings will be made when one unit is made to serve two spaces.

But for truly greater synergetic benefits other techniques beyond post-mounted meters should be considered. The interface of the parking-control

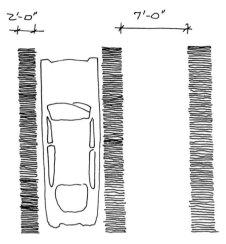

Broad bands are more effective than stripes in maintaining access space.

subsystem with other subsystems such as litter control and lighting offers an opportunity to share supports and installations. Many communities put waste receptacles on meter posts. Still other combinations are possible.

Parking meters are the literal modern equivalent of the old hitching post. The planner's problem is to keep them from being an imposition—to use them as punctuation rather than the statement of an old-fashioned environment.

Off-Street Parking

If downtown parking needs were met by ground-level car parks alone, they would cover nearly the whole area of the center city. Wheels without people can be more efficiently stored in multistory structures. The planning and design of these will not be covered here. Let us consider instead the furnishing of parking lots where essential.

Design parameters for off-street lots are derived from policy as well as traffic requirements and site conditions. An operating decision must be made on whether the lot is to be attendant or self-parking. If the lot is not to be free, then a pay procedure must be established; the alternatives include attendant collection, individual meters, and tollgate.

All lots, pay or free, require products, signing, and marking to improve utilization and reduce operating costs and mishaps. Their design and siting not only are dependent upon the parking concept but should be an integral part of it. Several studies published by the Eno Foundation for Highway Traffic Control detail lot planning for optimum speed of movement and maximum number of stall spaces. In order for this degree of efficiency to be achieved, various control devices frequently are necessary.

Use of space under North-South expressway for parking, Metropolitan Dade County, Justice Building.

In a pay unattended lot, a device is required for prevention of unauthorized entry or exit. Usually it is a lift arm, but it may be any form of gate or barrier. In some systems the car is driven onto a platform which must be shifted sideways in order for the car to proceed. In other systems entrance of the car into a space and over a treadle starts a timing device and raises the treadle to prevent car removal.

Treadles and moving floor surfaces have not proved satisfactory in cold-weather areas. Installation and maintenance costs are high. They require salting in winter, and are frequently damaged by snowplows. The more common device is the gate-arm barrier, which should contain the following features: thermostatically controlled heater for cold-weather operations, gate arm made of resilient material that will not damage a car on impact, and sensory device to retract the gate arm if it strikes the vehicle on descent. In addition, flexibility of mode of operation is desirable to provide options for free one-way traffic (for exit in single-lane operation of a small lot), two-way traffic, and controlled one-way traffic.

Unattended systems require insertion of coins, key, or card to activate the control station for operation of the barrier. Control (payment) may be established on entry or exit or both by buried presence sensors capable of directional sensing for automatic barrier actuation. Units should be positioned in advance of the barrier so the driver is not turning when alongside. Attended systems may issue parking checks manually or use a ticket dispenser. *A dispenser should issue one ticket per vehicle regardless of size or weight.* Entry lanes must be properly designed and marked. Widths have been increasing from 8 feet to as much as 13 feet. Stanchions or curbs may be necessary to keep motorists from damaging the equipment. These important visual elements should be carefully designed to assist the motorist in portal identification rather than merely act as barriers.

Traffic lanes may be established or delineated by low concrete islands separating stalls, or round plastic disks or pavement-mounted wheel barriers may be used. The front overhang of a car is approximately 3 feet; therefore a 6-foot median strip can be provided between parallel rows of parked cars without wasting space. Grass malls and trees can be used on the median. If medians are provided, 6-inch curbs are used for vehicle alignment. Without medians, raised guardrails are preferable to wheelstops, for easier snow removal.

The design of parking systems—efficient, esthetic, and integral with traffic systems—is a part of redeveloping the city. Parking areas must be linked to the places that generate the need for parking by direct and attractive pedestrian ways. The systems planning of facilities for parking access and storage will require systems design of supporting equipment also.

Chapter Six

Posts and Post Mortem

The most obvious and repetitive feature of the daytime environment is the array of poles, posts, and standards that support so many public products. We seem to want to put each light, signal, or sign on its own stick like a lollipop. But each pole is sited and installed without regard for the others or the total visual scene. Positioned along roads and walks the poles wall us in like a picket fence.

If well designed, these numerous elements can unify, organize, and provide continuity for the daytime image of the city. The lamppost can become the generative element of a new urban furniture system. Structure supporting necessary systems can be a handsome as well as useful linkage between man and his electromechanical environment.

But if lampposts are poorly designed, overcrowded, or inadequately chosen catalog items, they can make the city look slovenly and old-fashioned. Examination of their function and appearance, followed by redesign, is foremost in achieving overall environmental systems improvement.

Previous Practice

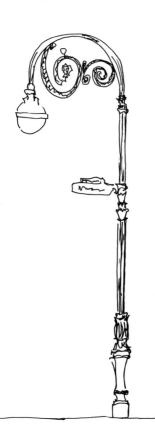

In the crudest form a light pole was (and in many areas still is) a pine tree with bark and branches lopped off and crossarm bolted on to support a lantern. Even when it was remotely fueled, its source of energy was carried externally until the late nineteenth century. Then the support assumed another function. It became additionally a hollowed, protective, housing carrier, or raceway, for distribution of the fuel—first gas, then electricity.

Posts and poles sprouted rapidly as cities grew. But their design parameters remained essentially the same. Function was still narrowly defined. The structure was still conceived as a tube, duct, or post with a single fixture perched on top or outthrust by bracket. Engineering was based on the manufacturers' traditional use of materials and the limited versatility of their production facilities.

As cities electrified, the light pole assumed still another function, that of image maker. It became a means of civic and business-district advertisement. In those cities using wood poles with overhead power distribution the message was "I am small, poor, or unaware." But the large, wealthy, sophisticated city displayed its preeminent position by installing custom-designed cast-iron columns.

The favored styles were based on classical motifs and usually featured an elaborately decorated pedestal supporting a fluted column terminating in an ogee-curve bracket; a most elegant variation of this style, the bishop's crook, is still seen and loved in some areas of Manhattan. As cities grew and took form, custom designs were installed downtown, with less expensive models doing service in the residential areas. Business districts vied with one another in efforts to have spectacular unique designs. In San Francisco one pridefully installed ornate-style lamppost, still treasured as a civic asset, was on Market Street, and another more appropriate style was displayed in Chinatown. Salt Lake City featured Indian heads on its posts.

Current Practice

Decorative styling is still the basis for the design of almost all downtown lampposts. In Chicago the brash commercialism of State Street is advertised with brutal, vulgar posts, while the style-aware North Michigan Avenue shopping district competes with more slender contemporary poles.

Although New York, with more than sixty-four different lamppost models in use, has attempted to standardize on the "Fifth Avenue standard," in most cities the installation of more single-purpose poles continues at an accelerated rate. Uncounted millions of single-function lampposts, signposts, and heavy-duty traffic poles to support span wire and signals are in use. Based on a nationwide survey by *The American City*, more than 5 million lighting poles alone are in use in American cities. And there are additional unknown millions of special-purpose poles and signposts. It is worth noting that residential streets account for 56 percent of the lighting poles, while business areas account for 16 percent. The balance are spread over highways, parks, and other undefined areas. Cities of exceptionally high density such as New York have only one-third the national average of poles per capita. But for other cities over 10,000 population, the density of light poles is about 48 per 1,000 people.

Clearly, lighting poles and other supports have become most significant and conspicuous elements in the cityscape. And concurrently their cost has increased. Over 500 thousand dollars was required to reequip the Downtown of Cincinnati, whose urban renewal project required 600 new light standards in 1969. Also, though lampposts are effective as machine-age totems, monumental symbols of city power, as long as this imagery remains unblemished and undiluted in impact, they have now been so festooned with signs and signals and other municipal junk that the imagery has changed to chaos and blight. Therefore the design problem now revolves about intensifying the community image, achieving synergetic benefits of cost savings, and reducing clutter. All three are not only desirable but essential.

PLANNING PUBLIC IMPROVEMENTS

Systems Layout

No one plants a pole without cause. The installation is subsidiary to a primary need for some other subsystem, such as lighting, information, or communications. Thus the structure is valueless in itself. Its worth—economic, esthetic, or functional—has value only to the extent that it acts in concert with other components and contributes to the whole. Another component may be completely integrated into the support, in which case structure and message, for example, are one. In addition to posts, sidewalk and street surfaces or something else may be the message carrier. Curbs can carry linear messages. New electronic and optical devices can be used as multichannel carriers.

Early in the planning phase, then, before freezing on any specific support or carrier, it is desirable to determine the various subsystems requirements. The lighting plan will determine the number and location of necessary supports. The traffic signing, street signing, transit information, and other visual signage will also require support. So will fire and police and citizen

Chinatown, San Francisco.

Lamp standard, Salt Lake City, Utah.

137

emergency-reporting equipment. All these composite needs should be shown on one overlay of the project site. The scope of support application will be evident. This "street-furniture plan" will show duplications and spatial overlaps. Improper locations can be adjusted and the plan revised to eliminate duplications and consolidate equipments on one support where possible.

Scale

Scale is not actual size, but apparent relative size, and most people instinctively sense this. A large overstuffed chair that appears gross and overimportant in a small room may appear opulent and appropriate in a larger space. Similar consumer reactions to size of fixtures should be considered in the furnishing of exterior space.

Scale of posts to the mass of nearby buildings can be predetermined. In certain areas of open spaces such as highway intersections and cloverleafs, few but high light towers may be appropriate. Along pedestrian walks posts should be small-scale, and the use of bollards could be considered. In any event a family relationship can be established between the various size units necessary to meet different needs throughout the city. Freeways, neighborhoods, and Downtown will each require light standards of different height and scale, but a continuity of community identity and greater sense of order can be provided by establishing a hierarchy of scale between posts, a related use of materials and color, and a continuity of shape.

SYSTEM DESIGN

Performance Criteria

The support components—foundation, base, shaft, and bracket, if any—should work as a unit, but their structural fundamentals will not be reviewed here. The relationship between structural behavior and structural form is important, but the relevant engineering data have been covered many times over elsewhere. Instead, systems criteria will be emphasized, with the following considered most meaningful. The support should:

1. Be multipurpose for utmost flexibility in accommodating varied component needs.

2. Be shaped to orient, index, and pre-position components for self-location and self-attachment.

3. Minimize wiring labor and facilitate plugging into.

4. Be producible by mass-production techniques.

After installation, continued systems performance demands a configuration adaptable to changing needs, thus minimizing the need for future poles and conserving space. Built-in flexibility versus immediate suitability poses the paradox of growth. The closer the designer gets to achieving the universal product grid, the farther he is from providing product spaces suited to specific needs. But signing needs will change. Lighting requirements are not static. Unknown devices to meet as yet unspecified needs will be installed in the next decade. Clearly the user will have less difficulty with the *multipurpose* pole in controlling equipment costs and maintaining integrity of environmental design.

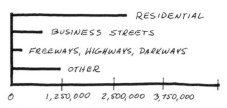

Distribution of lighting poles by area of city. Approximate national total 5 million units.

Other Design Goals

A favorable appearance is essential for consumer appeal, since the support structure's importance in shaping the urban synthetic environment is magnified by repetition as well as size. But what kind of imagery should the product have, and how is it to be achieved? Because of the need for precise component interface, cost control, and high-volume production, the most successful solutions will undoubtedly be shaped by machine tooling. Like consumer goods and private industrial products, public equipments must be attuned to the industrial process. And imaginative concepts need not be constricted. On the contrary, new dimensions for contemporary expression are made possible. Only the eclectic personalized designs requiring handcraft execution will be restricted.

Better design of the interface of support and sidewalk is essential. Present practice depends on the skill and interest of installation crews for adequate product placement and finished appearance. Excessive site work leads to crazy-quilt appearance of concrete work around post bases. The bolt-down hardware on catalog designs from industry is usually crude or poorly masked by decorative cover plates.

However, when floor interface is made part of the systems design, more ordered solutions become feasible. Fieldwork can be reduced through use of factory-made connectors. Where one-piece butt-base poles are inserted into the ground without concrete foundation, pre-positioning sleeves can be designed. Where posts are installed to transformer bases, anchor nuts can be tightened to studs within the vault. Where posts are bolted to concrete foundations, the installation can be recessed, with a flush cover making crisp and clean the intersection of post and floor. And numerous other possibilities, such as sliding collars, can be developed.

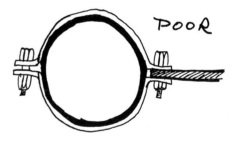

SOME CONCEPTS

Mast

Consider the soaring grace, economy of material, and sophistication of design embodied in the sailing-ship mast at the close of its history. Tall and strong but light in weight, it withstood the stress of wind and wave. Although it was firmly rooted, its flexibility of rigging met the varying loads and needs of the wind power system. By comparison how clumsy is the assemblage of booms, brackets, and span wire attached to most street-corner masts!

However, there is growing recognition of the need to carefully integrate components into support. Although the great majority of traffic signals, signs, streetlights, and transmission wires are still attached by means of brackets and bolts, more consideration is being given to coordinated shape, scale, and color.

Vertical Matrix

In the vertical matrix components are indexed, pre-positioned, and mated to each other by means of the plug-in rather than bolt-on. Although the vertical support can be compartmented into even modules with each space reserved for one component, more flexibility may be achieved by plugging components into the vertical frame where needed.

The vertical matrix with precision-shaped section is well adapted to the needs of certain precision components and to the machine demands of mass production. More than the simple round pole, the matrix shape tends to simplify installation and order the visual scene.

Horizontal Module

Where the quantity of street-furniture components exceeds the capacity of a single vertical support, an array of posts can be used. These may be pre-ordered within a fixed grid. In this process both the vertical position of

(Below, left) *Lamppost, Century City, Los Angeles. Sliding collar conceals bolts.* (Center) *Thirty-foot tapered, natural-finish lamppost, Sheraton Hotel, Prudential Center, Boston. Sliding plate conceals recessed bolts.* (Right) *Flagpole base, Civic Center, Chicago.*

Mizzenmast, U.S.S. Constitution.

components on the posts and the horizontal location of posts on the side-walk are preestablished. Problems of growth and the need to add more components are solved by filling more horizontal spaces. In practice, a por-tion of the pedestrian walk parallel to the street can be reserved as a *collector strip* for street furniture. Division of the linear strip into compartments pre-positions each component.

This modular arrangement results in a formalized layout whose conven-tional approach has traditional appeal. But the emphasis remains on prod-ucts, not people. The cityscape becomes rearranged for the convenience of machines, not according to use. And while this scheme may make more disciplined the visual scene, it has the disadvantage of perpetuating the use of great numbers of posts and separate units. Given the constant increase in number of equipments in the cityscape, this arrangement in not very skillful hands can result in the sidewalk fenced with an impenetrable picket of posts.

Cluster or Pod

Rather than string supports along the curb, the designer may gather components together and gang-plug them into the floor. Each element or post remains separate and can be optimized to its most efficient diameter and height as well as position. Components such as waste receptacles or fire hydrants can be integrated into the cluster. Hopefully, these are all tied together by the design of equally expressive shapes and by the manner of their placement in a high-density relationship surrounded by open space. Although the arrangement is asymmetric, the position of each element within the cluster must be predetermined for repetitive use. However, this scheme may appear less formal and more dynamic than the more obviously regimented collector strip, as well as permit a higher density of components necessary at street corners.

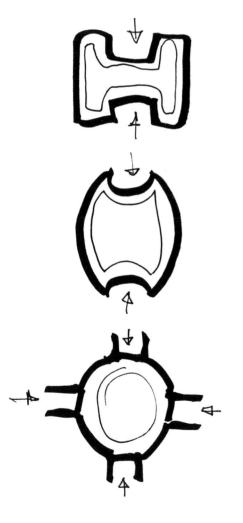

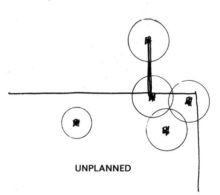

UNPLANNED

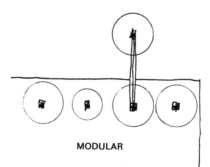

MODULAR

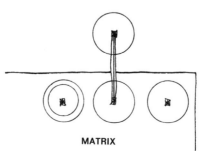

MATRIX

(Far left) *Possible pole sections that locate, index, and aid mounting of components.* (Left) *Same street intersection with different equipment arrangements.* (Below) *Street matrix that organizes cluster of poles.*

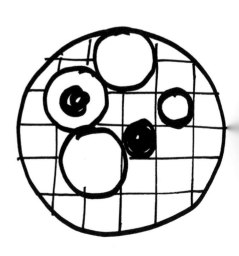

Multidimensional Space Frame

True spatial configurations will evolve from the analysis of the optimum spatial location of equipments, such as streetlights or traffic signals, and the development of a continuous structural shape, a multidimensional space frame, to support them there. This has already been tried on an experimental scale, and many variations can evolve and be used.

Such optimized use of three-dimensional space will become more frequent as designers, freed of conventional concepts of the static lamppost, exploit the full potential of technology and materials to place products in their appropriate place in space. In the nineteenth century new methods of calculation aided by improved ferrous metals conceived of structure as composed of linear elements. The behavior of forces moving in a prescribed direction could be measured and controlled in advance. But twentieth-century structural engineering is moving along other than linear paths. There is a tendency to activate every part of a structural system instead of concentrating the flow of forces into single channels—like posts. Designers can make these newer systems expand freely in all directions.

MATERIALS AND FINISHES

Evaluation Criteria

Contemporary technology affords the designer a wide choice of materials, the exotic as well as the traditional used in new ways. Previous criteria of

Model of space-frame experiment in stress-spun concrete, 1963.

choice have revolved about purchase and thirty-year maintenance costs. With growing recognition of the visual importance of the structural support and with a wider choice, the designer needs to select the appropriate material for the specific task based on additional criteria such as the following:

1. Compatibility with the reinforcement of community identity

2. Adaptability to mass production in achieving shape required by systems design

3. Compatibility with materials used in components to be supported

4. Resistance to destructive forces such as corrosion, vandalism, and vehicles

Safety

Most functional requirements for poles, such as roadway lighting or traffic signs, require placement at the curb in order to get most efficient use. This puts the lamp or sign where the action is but makes the pole hazardous to motorists. As an example, Buffalo, New York, a city of 500,000 population, experiences 600 "breakaways" per year when motorists strike steel light poles.

Previous engineering practice was to strengthen the pole to prevent damage. Since congressional hearings on highway safety have documented the hazard to motorists, emphasis has changed to protecting the driver. The designer now must relocate posts out of the way, choose a less rigid material, or integrate safety shear elements into the pole design.

Wood

About two-thirds of all poles in the city are presently wood, and this percentage may be as high as 80 percent in the smaller city. Each lasting about thirty-five years, wood poles still deliver 90 percent of the nation's electricity and are reportedly a 26-billion-dollar investment. Because the wood pole carrying a jungle of exposed wires typifies urban blight, development of more contemporary and less obtrusive support of overhead distribution wires has been sponsored by the American Wood Preservers Institute and the electric utilities.

OSAR (Overhead Systems Appearance Research) was one project dedicated to such development. Its goals were the esthetic improvement of poles and pole-top equipment. Systems criteria were proposed in order to assure economical and practical solutions to the goal of esthetic improvement in the residential environment. The criteria revolved about simplification and integration of wires to support. Desirable design practices dictated that the support structure should:

> Express its principal function.
> Reflect a visual integration of functional components.
> Express technological progress.
> Reflect provisions for special environmental conditions.

Many other innovative approaches to use of wood can be considered, such as lamination. Impregnated with resin and cured by heat and pressure, wood can be given additional properties that permit a greater variety of shape and section other than solid post. The potentiality of this machine-created material is largely unexplored, however, so cost is still high and acceptance low.

Cast Iron

The proportion of poles made of metal ranges from one-third in the larger cities to one-eighth in the smaller ones. Cast iron has been in use longer than any other noncombustible material. It offers many advantages, such as resistance to vandalism. The New York City Bureau of Gas and Electricity still uses it, for this reason, in the 10-foot pedestal size in the city parks. It can be produced in a variety of cross sections and shapes. It can be cast with integral butt end for easy ground installation and removal, and with integral collars and fixture adapters.

Park pedestals have been customarily painted in green enamel, a finish which is inexpensive and easy to maintain. But the designer should consider use of gray or other neutral colors when large posts are to be used on concrete walks or in urban settings.

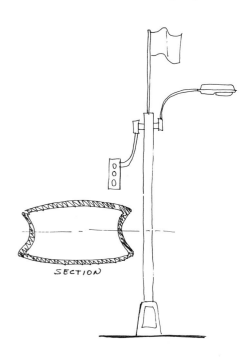

"Light tree" concept for downtown lighting.

(Right, above) *Fifth Avenue Standard with accessories.* (Below) *Fifth Avenue Standard, extruded aluminum shaft epoxy-welded to cast-aluminum base.*

Steel

Steel tubing is used almost three times as frequently as cast iron. Carbon steel offers low initial cost but possesses poor maintenance characteristics and shape potentiality. At greater cost, cold-rolled, fabricated, and welded sections of high-strength steel offer increased strength and configuration advantages. Color selection of paint on galvanized metal is good, and the post can be "painted out." An improved ten years life can be achieved by epoxy evaporation coatings, but these and similar films are subject to defacement. The "rusting" steels are a high-strength material, never need painting, and acquire a permanent patina of integral dark brown color expressive of the industrial process.

Aluminum

Presently used only half as frequently as cast iron, aluminum tubing is gaining acceptance for shopping centers, campuses, and civic areas as a single-purpose lamppost of contemporary appearance. The lamppost is most frequently seen as spun seamless tubing, tapered and/or bent. Utility has been limited by marginal structural characteristics. When davit shape has been used, motorist vertigo has been reported from observing pole sway induced by wind loading on the luminaire. Along with poor shear characteristics, electric conductivity may be a problem in areas of possible vehicular destruction. Thin-wall stems, supporting large globes, are vulnerable to vandalism.

The above deficiencies can be minimized through use of extruded shapes. And although the standard finishes seem obtrusive for most environments, other anodized or weather-resistant baked-enamel finishes could be used or developed. But the extensive systems possibilities of aluminum are largely unexplored, with the exception of the Fifth Avenue standard and an early 1959 prizewinning design by Jack Howe in England.

Concrete

Less than 10 percent of the poles in cities below 500,000 population are concrete, but the proportion rises to 27 percent in larger cities. Requiring no foundation, concrete poles are moderate in initial and maintenance costs and are therefore in greater use than steel in many residential areas and in areas where corrosion of steel is a problem. Older posts were made of reinforced static-cast concrete. By present-day criteria, these posts possess poor strength/weight and high water-absorption ratios. But concrete has been considerably improved in recent years, making it suitable for use in all areas of the city.

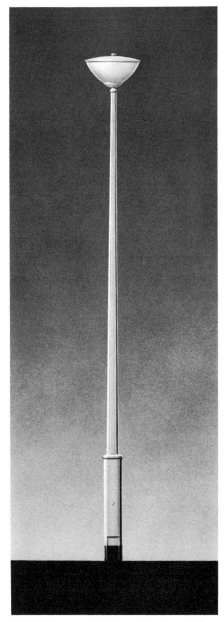

Fifteen-foot street-lighting unit, winner in 1959 competition by Aluminum Development Association. Features lightweight, tapered shaft made from parallel side extrusions cut diagonally, reversed, and epoxy-cemented together.

Centrifugal-cast concrete is one improvement. When the mix is pressure-pumped into a metal mold, then rotated at high speed, the mix is compacted. Excess water is spun to the center and removed, forming a nonconductive raceway for conduits. A dense, nonabsorbent surface, with integral color and aggregate effect, is obtained. Fittings may be cast as inserts. Also, the butt may be integral-cast, therefore eliminating cost of foundation work and anchoring.

Prestressed concrete makes possible an even stronger structure for severe applications. During manufacture of prestressed-concrete poles, high-tensile steel wires are attached to anchorages at either end and positioned in the mold. Predetermined stresses are introduced, directly opposed to those the mast or standard will receive. The mold is then revolved at high speed. Several manufacturers produce these poles, cost-competitive with steel and less costly than aluminum, in larger sizes.

Plastics

Fiber glass, filament-wound glass, and reinforced resin offer improved structural strength, integral color, and nonconductivity. Small-scale lampposts made of these materials are now in service in England and gaining increased acceptance on the Continent. The attraction of plastic for the designer is largely in the variety of contours possible for enhanced performance or imagery and achieved in mass production by use of mold or mandrel.

Trefoil shape produces lightweight column easily removed from concrete mold.

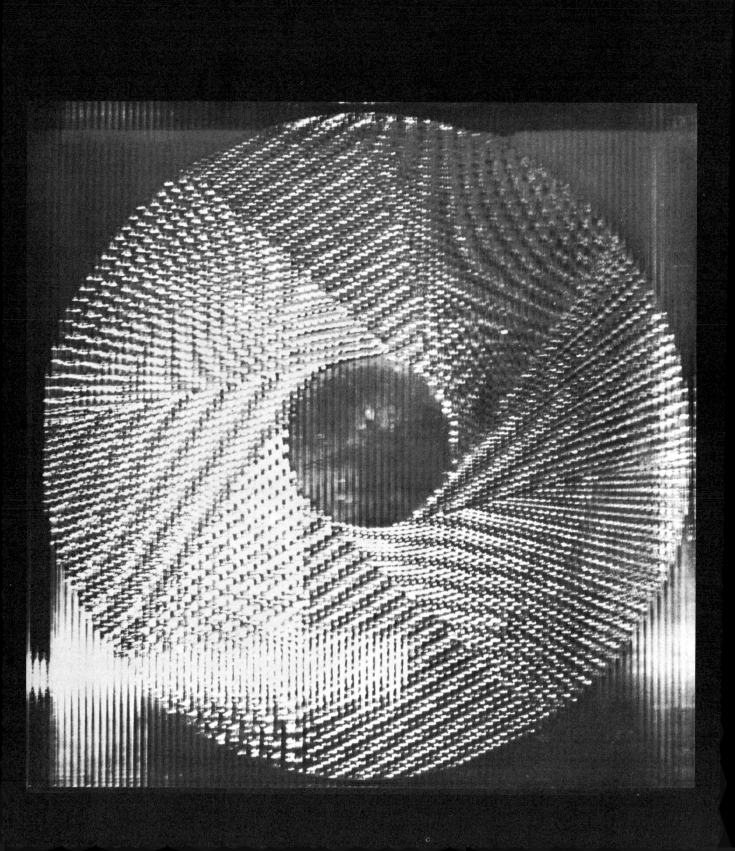

Chapter Seven

City Lights

Light is frequently referred to as a tool. It is not. Light is a raw material similar to space. The designer has to push it around. He has to determine what light is, how to use it, where to put it. His tools of manipulation are lamps and luminaires.

By day, sunlight covers all and sunlight is free. By night, artificial light is isolated, spotty, and costly. Artificial light is a commodity metered and dispensed by light fixtures which are the most obvious product in the nighttime environment.

Previously designers have been primarily concerned with improvement of lighting fixtures for interior use. There are now many instances where special designs for exterior use can be economically justified because of better interface with other products and systems or improvement of imagery.

Previous criteria of evaluation of light in public places have been based on a formula whose factors are dollars and footcandles. Historically, people have demanded (and paid for) more and more light to provide security and a sense of place. Reduction of vehicular accidents and speedup of traffic have recently been added as objectives. The engineer has always been concerned with amount and placement of light; now the designer has a role—to satisfy human needs through the lighting system.

A TALE OF TWO CITIES . . . AND THEN SOME

Folklore is full of stories about cavemen finding fire to be a protection from prowling enemies and animals. Other legends tell us how more sophisticated uses of firelight evolved as society developed and moved into settlements and towns. Fire-filled iron baskets, oil lamps, then candles came into use. Each offered a bit more light or a bit less maintenance. The torchbearer or lantern bearer became a status symbol for those travelers who could afford him. The psychological and inspirational values of outdoor artificial light were recognized in towns; as early as 1417, the lord mayor of London ordered that lights be hung out on winter evenings between "Hallowtide and Candlemasse."

As the civilized world grew in size and sophistication, communities took over from the individual the responsibility for providing lanterns, for community safety and prestige. In 1666 Paris passed a street-lighting tax, whose proceeds provided 6,500 lanterns lighted twenty times a month (moonlight presumably illuminated the other ten nights). In 1738 London installed 15,000 oil lamps and in 1809 the first gas lamps. Gas was so superior and so much cheaper a fuel that the gas lamp quickly became the standard around the world, with the Baltimore installation of 1815 the first in America.

Other technical improvements followed, and cities quickly accepted them because of the increasing cost of lighting the increasing miles of residential streets as well as Downtown. Edison's carbon-filament arc light was more efficient than the gas lamp, and the tungsten-filament gas-filled incandescent lamp of 1915 was more economical than the arc light.

Spurred by citizen demand for status and/or crime prevention, our cities continued to add more and brighter lamps through the roaring twenties until the Great Depression. Now, forty years later, they still possess the same hodgepodge of posts, lamps, and luminaires—except for a few cities where aggressive merchants or public works people have upgraded lighting facilities to more contemporary levels. But even these special projects have usually had design parameters built around quantity, not quality, of light.

The story is told in Chicago that when State Street installed its glaring high-intensity lighting, "It became bright enough for you to read the serial number on the hoodlum's nickle-plated gun." Brightness alone does not cure crime. A more effective way to minimize crime on the streets is to get more people into an area, on the sidewalks, coming and going. And the way to achieve this is to build up the quality of the light and environment, not merely to put up more and more lights.

(Above) *Lexington, Massachusetts.* (Left)
Niagara Falls, New York.   152

Lighting can be, by its nature, an inherent shaper of urban form. Handsome lighting in an area attracts large numbers of people to it for work or play. Amusement parks and automobile sales agencies demonstrated the emotional magic and attraction of artificial light long ago. But until now lighting engineers have designed new systems by the narrow formula of dollars and footcandles. They have ignored the primeval potential of warm light to attract people and influence urban development as something beyond the scope of their responsibilities.

The urban designer or multidisciplinary team has no such limitations. But nothing constructive will happen until we realize that every true metropolis has two cities downtown—the daytime city and the nighttime city. Revitalization of the daytime city with new office buildings, banks, and plazas means nothing at five o'clock when everybody pours out and goes home to the suburbs. What happened to the nighttime city? It is dark and deserted. True urban areas like Tokyo, London, and Berlin have nighttime cities that are active and alive. Public lighting and signage contribute to that atmosphere. Making the nighttime city successful is a prime challenge for the environmental designer.

"Cherry Picker" is used to service high-mounted, high-output fluorescent lamps, State Street, Chicago.

THE HUMAN EXPERIENCE

How We See

There is so much emphasis on the quantity of light that it needs remembering that usually people don't see illumination at all—only brightness. As William M. C. Lam points out, "We all know that light is a form of energy which, when radiated to a given point, produces illumination at that point. The significant fact, though, is that we can't see this light until it is intercepted by our eyes." This means that unless the observer is looking directly at the light source, he sees only the light retransmitted, or reflected, by surfaces around him. This light is brightness, not illumination.

Accordingly, man interprets what he sees in terms of brightness. Obviously, then, this brightness is not an *absolute* but an *apparent* brightness of object or surface. It may be considerably modified by surrounding objects and surfaces as well as the total brightness of the scene—night or day.

Many of us forget to compensate for this effect when using the camera, for example, and ruin photographs. A great variation in lens opening or shutter speed is required for photographing a model on a grassy knoll as compared with a sandy beach, where overexposure usually prevails. The amount of light may be the same, but the reflectivity of sod is certainly much less than that of sand.

Carried to excess, brightness is glare. There is directed glare from an unshielded light source. There is reflected glare from glossy or shiny surfaces and objects in the environment. Glare interferes with vision and causes eye discomfort. In seeing, the effect of glare is a loss of contrast between detail and background. Contrast is important because the basis for seeing at any level of illumination is reasonable contrast in brightness or hue.

How Much Light

In full daylight, brightness differences of 2 to 4 percent can be discriminated. At dusk, the contrast has to be as much as 60 to 70 percent. This ability to distinguish fine details, or visual acuity, becomes important when reading, say, a traffic sign. Because committees that formulate lighting standards are task-oriented rather than people-oriented, the technical criteria frequently revolve about how high a degree of visual acuity is desirable and therefore how much illumination is necessary to ensure that level.

Are there any absolute criteria of value in designing outdoor lighting? First consider *indoor* lighting. Footcandle levels are based on the amount of illumination required to produce brightness that enables people to see their tasks clearly and comfortably. (A footcandle of illumination falling on a surface with 100 percent reflectance produces a footcandle of brightness.) The criteria for indoor needs relate to definition of task, task difficulty, and degree of required visibility. The illumination required for visibility is related to the size and contrast of the task, as well as its complexity. Therefore there are many variables of problems, which in turn pose many alternatives of solution.

But in discussions of *outdoor* lighting tasks have not been defined. Indeed, a survey of the literature indicates little consensus on the importance of the various factors involved in satisfying visibility requirements. It is not always known precisely how much illumination is required for each different mission. Selection of lighting levels is arbitrary. And artificial-light minimums have been rising as rapidly as the national gross product.

Example: State Street, Chicago. A 1958 merchant-sponsored project featured huge fluorescent fixtures producing 15 footcandles.

Example: City of Chicago. Voters approved a 20-million-dollar bond issue for more lighting to reduce crime. Then 51,000 mercury lights were

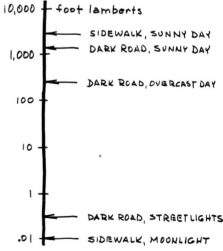

Commonly experienced brightness levels.

installed in 2,300 alley-miles, 1,800 lights on streets which had none, 3,800 additional lights on arterial-street approaches.

Example: New York City spent 65 million dollars through the 1960s to modernize 5,600 miles of streets and 500 miles of park footpaths. An attempt was made to standardize sixty-four different types of installations using 210,000 lamps of varied wattage.

Example: St. Louis in 1964 started a ten-year program to relamp 280 street-miles. Fixtures of 1926 vintage in 10 central business district (CBD)-miles were replaced with luminaires producing 12 foot-candles.

Example: Cedar Rapids, Iowa. Thousand-watt fixtures mounted at 30 feet, each providing 60,500 lumens and yielding 8 footcandles, replaced thirty-five-year-old fixtures in the CBD which had a delivery of 0.25 footcandles from 10,000 to 15,000 lumens light sources.

Example: Appleton, Wisconsin, relighted, changing from 0.8 footcandles to 12 footcandles with Lucalox luminaires 100 feet apart on two sides of street. Time clock turns off one side at midnight. Photocells turn off other side not on clock.

Example: Rockford, Illinois. Twenty square blocks of the central area were relighted to 18 footcandles.

A city whose Downtown has been illuminated at a level of 0.25 foot-candles for thirty years may decide to install a new lighting system. But what level will be appropriate for the next twenty or thirty years—7 footcandles, 15 footcandles, 30 footcandles? Is the quantity of the utmost importance? I think not. For the important criterion really is how well the overall lighting system enhances the observer's appreciation of the nighttime city.

Outdoors at night we are constantly scanning our surroundings in order to orient ourselves. But usually there is not a specific viewing task at all. Therefore the primary need to be satisfied is the *comfort* of the viewer and his *pleasure* in seeing the environment.

Lam tells us that visual comfort in lighting has two main determinants, "the brightness ratio and what you are trying to see." This means that people can still walk in comfort and security on a dark night with a level of light which while low illuminates details and makes the objects around us brighter than the sky. We are interested in seeing these objects because they define the environment, and having just enough lighting to make this task easy also makes us more comfortable.

This may be why we are comfortable when viewing a city bathed in 10,000 footcandles of sunlight and yet prone to think a nighttime scene too bright if viewed at 15 footcandles. Perhaps the reason one street may seem too bright and harsh at 15 footcandles is that the adjacent street registers only little better than moonlight, 0.02 footcandles on the sidewalk. When mo-

Expo 67, Montreal. Projection lamps create interesting glow in filament-wound glass tubes and exciting patterns on adjustable plastic reflectors.

torists drive from commercial to residential street or pedestrians walk from space to space, the light they need to see by is affected by the previous brightness level.

The need for lighting must be established before it is designed or engineered. Imaginative and expansive lighting effects can do more than light the way for the observer. The influence of light on the culture and psychology of man is too great for it to be treated mechanically. The plastic value of artificial light should be used to sustain and enhance the imagery of structure and space. This requires a creative plan even more imaginative than the concept of "painting" with light, as in the theater.

Much can be learned from theatrical use of light and color to stimulate or control emotion and give pleasure. But flood-lighting of buildings, like stage lighting, is unidirectional, static, and not the answer. In the theater the audience sits in darkness and looks at the bright action. In the city the audience *is* the action. Spatial needs of the nighttime environment require three-dimensional modeling of the public right-of-way and the people in it. The question is not only how the environment looks but also how the audience of observers looks and feels.

PROGRAMMING LIGHT

What Is the Problem?

Whether a nighttime scene looks bright or dark often depends on where you are. From an airplane the lights of Downtown and even the neighborhoods appear to be brilliant multicolored jewels strewn on the blue-velvet carpet of night. But on the ground and walking the same streets, the space may seem dark, drab, and colorless. Lighting is important for psychological and commercial persuasion—for convincing people that it really is all right to be *here*, for discouraging crime, for encouraging business—and in view of this it ought to be frankly designed more from the commercial and psychological point of view than the technical. Usually the need is to find a way to maximize nighttime use of space. The problem frequently is this: *how can the cost of light be made to buy a nighttime image of suitable consumer appeal?*

With the problem posed in this manner, the designer has more options. He is free to program the need for color, location, and variation in light as well as intensity. He can be more innovative in creating solutions that please people. Although certain features may lead to an increase in total project cost, it is entirely possible that this approach, by extending public usage of facilities, will result in a reduction in cost per participant.

The renewal of large segments of the city and building of new towns, campuses, shopping centers, and airports—these present unrivaled opportunities for character building through nighttime lighting. Each neighborhood in each city will have its own specific needs and problems, but a generalized lighting program might emphasize goals similar to the following:

1. Develop a system which expresses the unique character of the area and the ambitions of its people.

2. Define the organization of streets and circulation.

3. Provide essential information about the immediate area to all users of the public right-of-way.

4. Contribute to the overall orientation of the public in order to enable people to find their way about the city.

5. Achieve synergetic benefits by packaging other subsystems such as communications with lighting for structure and utility sharing.

The analysis of such goals will determine whether 10 footcandles of street lighting is too much or too little for, say, the city core. If the purpose is to emphasize and separate the main shopping street from the surrounding frame, this is not too much. If the goal is to prevent accidents, it may be too much.

Pedestrian Needs

Historically, in addition to crime prevention, the chief justification for public lighting has been to provide enough visual information for pedestrians to use the city at night with safety. Plainly put, at night the artificial-light pattern is the city, shopping center, or campus. When daytime visual cues are absent, the designer must determine the amount and kind of light material necessary to communicate facts to an observer regarding the organization and character of the space.

By this standard, the pedestrian requires far more guidance than he now gets from public lighting. Certain pedestrian points—crosswalks, bus stops, park exits—could be better identified. This cannot be achieved by rote in a mechanical way. Linear patterns of equally spaced light sources of equal

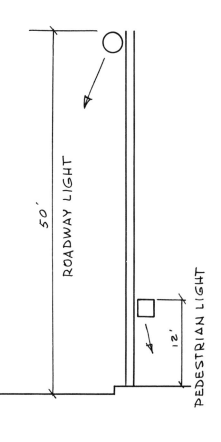

Oakland Mall, California. Cosmetic beautification.

intensity do not provide accents. The designer should analyze the space in terms of user needs and add these personalized improvements at small additional cost. The present monolithic single-purpose lighting system of most cities—high-mounted, roadway-oriented, high-wattage lamps—does not serve the dual needs of pedestrian and motorist. A multipurpose system can be evolved using a variety of lamps and components which will more realistically light city space in all its variations.

In the neighborhoods the pedestrian still requires light to illuminate his path and show obstacles, but his needs are primarily psychological. A sense of security is all-important. Shadowed areas may appear sinister. Whether in a large open space or in a narrow confined passage, there must be enough light to eliminate fear and provide reassurance.

Scale and design of pedestrian lighting are intimately related to human needs and directly influence emotions and actions. Warmth of light and a personalized atmosphere are essential. The use of indirect lighting or possibly low-wattage units closely spaced could be considered.

Formal plazas and courts may require psychological reinforcement of the active communal nature of the concourse or promenade. The basic concept of promoting activity may best be furthered by higher footcandle levels obtained from more frequent spacing of light sources.

Walks and stairs can be delineated with brighter lighting. But obtrusive fixtures or clusters on high stems are not essential. Optically engineered reflectors of hidden light can wash desired areas with light while leaving dramatic contrast in surrounding areas. Localized illumination can accent planter areas. Lighting may be recessed in steps, curbs, or balustrades where deep snow is not a problem.

In parks or on campus walks, the lighting problem is again psychological in nature. Warm accents of very low intensity are needed at close intervals to minimize shadows and therefore provide protection and a feeling of reassurance. Light sources should be low to maintain pedestrian scale. A linear line of light is desirable. However, intersections might have increased wattage for definition. The effect would be one of varying-size pools of light.

Motorist Needs

Roadway-lighting needs are not static. Even a single-purpose expressway has dynamic loading characteristics that change from hour to hour and mile to mile. A lighting system designed yesterday will surely not be adequate throughout its thirty-year life-span. The city is a kaleidoscope of lighting patterns. Design of the system requires analysis of the various land-use interfaces. Clearly the needs of various commercial and residential streets must be defined before performance criteria can be established and, finally,

Harvard Yard, Cambridge, Massachusetts.
Ever-popular scale and shape for pedestrian
precincts; 9 feet high.

160

Light, garden stairs, Lincoln Center, New York.

Lights, Habitat stairs, Expo 67, Montreal.

fixtures designed or selected. Strangely, this is not usual practice. Expressway lighting, for example, is a common need which seldom receives analysis and solutions according to changing road-use conditions.

The proper lighting of roadways can do much to provide the nighttime driver with visual cues and increase safety. Of especial importance are the entrances and exits onto highways, where consideration should be given to providing transitional lighting. The environmental change may be marked by color and/or intensity change. Doubled or different light sources may be used.

Forests of lampposts presently are used to light complex road junctions, producing a confusing array of light sources. This jumble of lights without clear pattern provides no visual cues, and the road is made hazardous by the great number of massive posts placed so close to the right-of-way. But in Europe, high-mast lighting schemes are being introduced to reduce the number of columns while maintaining good illumination. These are commonsense results of the correct analysis of, say, a cloverleaf as a spatial experience and not merely a node on a linear path.

One such system, supplied by Osram (GEC) Ltd., has been used for the Cumberland Basin Bridges scheme in Bristol. Conventionally about 160 lampposts would have been required. But only thirty masts, each one 82 feet high and equipped with four lanterns housing 1,000 watts of mercury lighting, were installed. The masts are of steel, the lanterns of aluminum. By use of winches (internal in the mast), lantern maintenance can be carried out at ground level.

Reduction of accidents on highways is a dramatic benefit of good lighting but not the only one. When an expressway is properly lighted, the safe driving speed at night can be 10 to 20 miles per hour higher. If the arterial speed limit is raised 15 miles per hour because of improved nighttime conditions, greater utilization of lanes can be achieved and significant savings can accrue in economic value of time saved per vehicle. Highway capacity is also increased by better motorist performance—for example, greater use of passing opportunities, improved utilization of interchanges, reduction in fatigue and tension.

Downtown

When the roadway enters the central business district, a new space is penetrated and new criteria must be established. The need is not just to increase brightness, but rather to create a mood of excitement and gaiety and an identity sufficiently unique to achieve a public response of commercial value.

Congested places of public activity such as downtown shopping or

Routine textbook approach to roadway lighting. Redundant, confusing, hazardous.

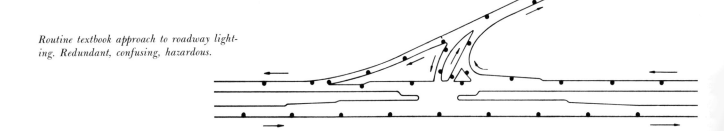

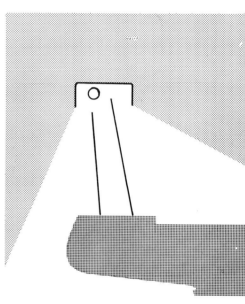

(Above, left) *Fort Washington Highway,
Cincinnati, Ohio. Results of textbook approach. Redundant, confusing, hazardous.*
(Opposite) *GEC system. English-designed
light interchange with light fixtures clus-
tered on four masts.* (Above) *Strip lighting integrated with center-median
guardrail or bridge railing, as in San
Mateo–Hayward Bridge or La Guardia Airport upper ramp.*

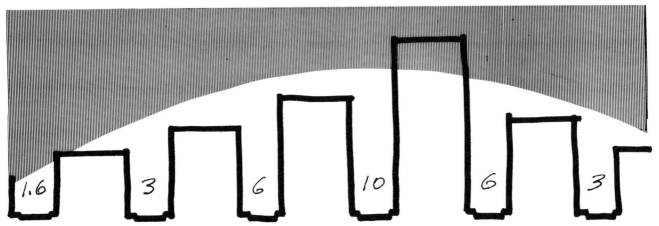

The nighttime city highlighted with transition from the 1.6 footcandles of Downtown to 10 footcandles in the Cincinnati core.

"Sun of the Sea," aluminum and glass.

amusement centers require a different design approach with even more emphasis on animation and mood. Characteristics of excitement, gaiety, opulence, and novelty may all have varying application. Very likely a lighting plan of only one brightness level will not be successful; variation is required to heighten the anticipation of the observer and to mark his arrival at the city's core.

At main intersections, changes in lighting can be purposefully and logically introduced. Light sources can be varied in height, color, intensity, or spacing to mark intersections and nodes. Monotony is relieved, identification achieved, and safety enhanced by manipulating light to signal potential danger points. And as the road changes and becomes residential in character, a new analysis is required which differs from that of arterial roads or Downtown.

I applied these principles in Cincinnati "Streetscape." Starting at an existing base level of 0.8 footcandles for the city at large, illumination was increased to 1.6 footcandles in the downtown frame, 2.5 footcandles in the inner ring of streets, 5 footcandles in the center city, and 10 in the city core of twelve blocks.

While those levels are not high by tomorrow's standards or even those of today, the variation provides transition. A balance is achieved between dramatic effects and pushing back the darkness.

The most significant changes and ideas, however, are yet to be tried. This will occur when a city is bold enough to program its downtown lighting for constantly changing kinetic effect. If the goal is truly the stimulation of the observer, then obviously static linear lighting, no matter how bright, is not enough. We should look to a more fluid use of lighting—enlarging, shrinking, twinkling—rather than fixed and constant street sources. There is a potential for instant beauty in urban lighting that can be achieved by projection of optical effects and colors on the public right-of-way and spaces. Lights can be *programmed* to tell time by flashing, the number of flashes corresponding to the hour. And even rhythm can be introduced, through programmed modulation or dimming of supplementary light sources, to create a sense of movement.

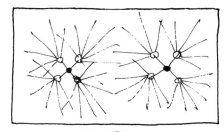

POOR

Parking

Since vehicle lights are directional and not always present, general illumination is required for security and safety in parking lots. Omnidirectional lighting tends to reduce shadows and concealment for vandalism. Center-post systems should be considered. Posts might be located within a distance twice the mounting height from the area perimeter. Post spacing does not normally exceed four times mounting height.

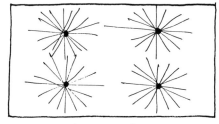

COMMON

Parking garages present different problems, with consideration required for the effect of simultaneous viewing of interior and exterior. Programming can establish the need for, say, a dual electric system of fluorescent lighting which would give greater intensity during the day to avoid excessive contrast with the open sky.

DESIGNING THE URBAN LIGHTING PLAN

Scale

Both client and designer of interior space understand that various lighting techniques and tools are necessary to enhance interior space and make it work. Such understanding needs to prevail in relation to exterior space too. In furnishing this space, the creative designer will prepare a schematic concept which utilizes all possible techniques that best satisfy the functional criteria. The need is great. In contrast to the private sector, where the designer controls all building elements, in the public sector lighting is frequently the only means available for expression of the nighttime city.

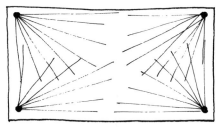

EFFICIENT

One approach would be to develop the design concept and then the fixturing according to a hierarchy of scale. In addition to brightness variation by means of different light sources, variation in mounting height might differentiate the nighttime use of major arteries, second-degree collector streets, commercial streets, residential streets, and parks.

It seems obvious that commercial-size poles and high-wattage lamps should not be used in residential streets. Yet in dozens of American cities old cast-iron low-scale units of pedestrian scale and charm are being replaced by commercial-size fixtures whose uncontrolled beams concentrate glare and high intensities under the pole. In the private sector, developers of housing tracts frequently select oversize commercial fixtures assuming them to be newer and more efficient. Or they may select underscaled mock-colonial gas lamps (electrified) under the assumption these are more esthetic. Clearly not enough emphasis has been placed on variation in mounting height and scale of fixtures to area or mass of buildings as a design factor as important as the luminaire itself.

Siting

Spacing is related directly to mounting height and scale. The present practice is to draft the lighting system by projecting light-distribution patterns on a plan at ground zero. When they overlap, the spacing between units is established. This is essentially a linear process of stringing equidistant light sources along a utility line parallel to a road or path. But this practice does not utilize to best advantage the essential three-dimensional characteristic of light. To do this, intervening space, people, and illuminated objects must be considered as well as the roadway. The designer tied to a post by a utility line is not free, but captive. He lacks the chance for independent design action.

A more satisfactory design approach would be to consider variation in lateral areas as well as make bright the longitudinal spacing along the road. Interesting lateral lighting can be achieved by varying the Illuminating Engineering Society (IES) light-distribution pattern of selected units at nominal cost or by adding supplementary units placed as spurs to the main line of lights. Or better yet, a more versatile and interesting arrangement can be secured through the development of a flexible lighting system whose lamps are variable and adjustable in position rather than fixed.

After preparation of the preliminary plan, locations should be checked against other subsystem plans (communication, traffic, etc.) for possibilities in sharing of structure, conduits, and other facilities.

Lightmarks

Punctuation marks make intelligible a sentence; "lightmarks" identify a space and clarify the confusion of the city. Lightmarks serve more as accents than as sources of illumination. They can denote changes in the spatial use with varying degrees of emphasis. They can serve as nighttime landmarks. Each designer can construct his own design vocabulary of symbols. I suggest only a few possibilities here.

Nodelights   Lights of distinctive color or shape can be repetitively used throughout the city to locate street intersections and guide drivers through them.

Pylons   Structures of great height can identify arterial interchanges by

Schematic model of pedestrian and roadway lighting, streetscape program, Cincinnati, Ohio. Adjustable fixtures permit "trimming" the street for variable needs and effects.

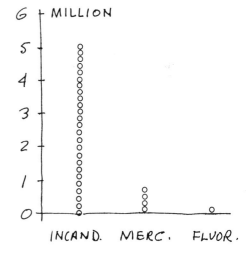

(Left) *Birmingham University precincts.*
(Below), *Proportion of lamp use in city lighting. 1963 data.*

day and support illuminated route markers visible for great distances by night.

Twinning   Like quotation marks, paired lights before and after can set apart a particular area from the great mass of space.

Street-furniture identification   To provide counterpoint to the main lighting scheme, various street-furniture elements can be usefully illuminated. Street signs at intersections could be self-illuminated to advantage; fire-alarm and citizen emergency-reporting telephones should have distinctive lighting.

Directories   Information centers sited at strategic points can display data on large illuminated panels. Transit and street-layout maps can present information to motorists or pedestrians.

Bollards   Selection of light fixtures is not limited to stem-mounted sources. Light at low level, seen only in the immediate area, can define a parking area or special space reserved for pedestrians.

LIGHTING SYSTEM COMPONENTS
Lighting Sources

The terminus of the system, the component in direct relationship to the consumer, is the light source itself. Yet it is the least satisfying element both in daytime appearance and nighttime quality. Unlike the sun and moon, to whose purity and power men respond, artificial light sources are frequently cheapened by excessively styled luminaires and lamp holders.

Most of America is still lighted by products reflecting needs and tastes of thirty years ago. Historically a product attitude has prevailed in a situation where process has been the mode of activity. The designer must now find a way to meet the need of planner, developer, or bureaucrat for an environment which satisfies emerging urban patterns of life.

Let's start with basics. In the choice of a lamp to light the city, it seems reasonable to start with a light source whose makeup as closely as possible approximates natural daylight. Other lamps may be used for accents, special purposes, or supplementary lighting, but the prime goal should be a lighting system which both clarifies the environment and bathes people with light in a pleasant and healthful way. By these criteria the majority of lamps currently favored are inadequate and obsolete.

We know from recent medical research that light affects health. The spectral characteristics of the light source affect certain glands as well as contribute to the seeing process. Natural light containing vitamin D produces direct photobiological effects by skin absorption; it also produces indirect effects upon the neuroendrocrine system by entering the eye.

If we consider afresh what people are going to expect from their public environment in the future, the importance of these phenomena becomes clear. As the trend to urbanization continues and people continue to spend their workdays at indoor tasks, they will want additive light sources that promote health and suntanning at night. As medical knowledge warrants, the lighting industry will be required to provide ultraviolet wavelengths and full-spectrum sources simulating the beneficial effects of natural light.

But what lighting criteria actually prevail now, and what are their results? Go back to Edison's first carbonized-thread lamp. It burned forty hours. The big things then were lamp life and output. These are still the criteria. Incandescent, the most desired and liked source for its warm sunlight-like quality, is rapidly losing ground to more sterile sources less costly to operate. Although American cities are still lighted four-fifths by incandescent sources as compared with one-fifth by mercury-vapor and fluorescent, this ratio applies primarily in residential areas. Because downtown merchants want brighter illumination at low cost, they are given mercury-vapor lamps. Even

Chocolate and silver-foil kisses. Streetlights, Hershey, Pennsylvania.

in neighborhoods, because of fear of crime and vandalism, emphasis on brightness rather than quality prevails.

It remains for the designer, then, to encourage developments which will satisfy all aspects of our changing needs. Selection from existing sources might be based on consideration of the following product characteristics:

Incandescent lamps are a point from which light rays are directed. Objects are accentuated by highlights and shadows. Modeling and texture are revealed. The sparkling quality provides a psychologically satisfying buoyant effect.

Several types offer low initial cost of wiring, installation, and equipment. Axial or standard filament construction in clear or inside-frosted bulbs requires the use of appropriate reflectors or high mounting. White-bowl lamps improve lighting quality by reducing shadows and glare. Street-series lamps are used in systems operating a number of lamps in an electric series connection with a high-voltage source. Light output remains constant. Output is described in lumens rather than wattage, and lamp life is rated at 2,000 hours. Multiple-street lamps are used in systems operating a number of lamps in an electric parallel connection with a standard or low-voltage power source. Light output is indicated in wattage, and lamp life is usually rated at only 1,500 hours.

Quartz-iodine filament tubes are a newer form of incandescent tube typically used in 500-watt or 1,500-watt ratings for floodlighting. They should be considered for other applications as well because of high efficiency, longer lamp life, higher light output throughout lamp life, and overall costs lower than those of conventional bulbs.

Mercury-vapor lamps, like incandescent, are directional and have a sharp sparkling quality. High-intensity mercury lamps trade off a drop in light quality for lower operating and maintenance costs. These lamps have higher initial equipment and installation costs, and glare is difficult to control where low mounting is required.

But lamp life is much longer than that of incandescent lamps. Mercury-vapor lamps furnish up to 2.5 times more light per power consumed than incandescent lamps. Replacement is simple with their screw or plug-in base. Lamps of 400 watts in refracted glassware will produce 20,000 lumens output (such as may be required at nodes or important circulation areas). Lamps of 175 watts in open reflectors or plastic globes can produce 7,700 lumens, a quantity of light more suitable for dormitory and neighborhood areas. Moreover, a lamp rated at 16,000 hours will at the end of 8,000 hours still be producing at 90 percent rated lumen output. However, a ballast or transformer and a constant-current regulator are required. If a ballast is used, choice must be made between internal (transformer base or luminaire) and external location and housing.

Factors to be evaluated in selecting the mercury-vapor lamp as opposed to other sources are desired daytime configuration and installation and maintenance costs. Poor color quality has been a factor in the past, but the color-corrected (phosphorcoated) lamp has eliminated much of the unnatural color distortion of the standard silver-white lamp.

Fluorescent lamps produce lighting that is flat and dull; dark objects in particular do not show up in detail, but are seen only in silhouette. These lamps offer low surface brightness and therefore have particular application where low mounting heights are required. Light can be produced in all sections of the visible spectrum, and designs have improved color characteristics, but the standard tube produces a light deficient in reds and blues which exaggerates blues and greens. Fluorescent is essentially flat in quality because of the nondirectional source.

High-output lamps are used for street lighting. These range from 100 watts or 6,600 lumens to high-intensity 200 watts or 15,000 lumens. The operating cost is low, and the light-producing efficiency is high except in cold weather, when output drops. The tubes have a long-rated life, at 7,500 hours, and require minimal maintenance.

Metal-arc multivapor lamps produce a warm white directional light which is noticeably different from that of the fluorescent or sodium-vapor lamp. A translucent aluminum oxide ceramic tube may be used to activate metal vapors at higher temperatures than previously possible. A 400-watt lamp is rated at 105 lumens per watt, and life expectancy is 6,000 hours. The increased efficiency is achieved without increased operating cost as compared with the mercury-vapor lamp.

Luminaires

The luminaire packages and protects the light source; by night it may also perform some additional function such as modification or control of light.

Although the majority (68 percent) of fixtures are glass-enclosed (23 percent glass open bottom, 2 percent plastic-enclosed, 7 percent other), fixtures come in all sizes and shapes. As the most visible element of the daytime cityscape, they have an importance for imagery that has always been well recognized. The octagonal streetlamps in Trafalgar Square, London, originally were used as lanterns on Admiral Nelson's flagship in the Battle of Trafalgar. Streetlights are still the one element of street furniture which frequently arouses the interest of local groups such as businessmen, who sponsor distinctive designs. The package has become the product, and no shape seems too bizarre. The effect upon the public of these "Mickey Mouse" fixtures, sometimes shocking in their size or novelty, has been startling in intensity. Passions have been aroused. Letters to the editor are written. Street lighting, it seems, has often produced more heat than light. But why not these unique designs?

Some communities are noted for a particular feature which can be characterized or memorialized by a reminiscent or evocative shape. Some business districts may want unique designs which express to the consumer the particular nature and advantages of the area. When repeated in procession down the street, like packages on a shelf, the symbol assumes potent advertising value, presenting and then again presenting the desired image to consumers, local and transient alike.

Like banal supermarket packages, luminaires can also proclaim mediocrity. Murphy's law might be amended to read, "Whenever the wrong catalog design is available, it will be selected." But when the urban designer elects to join the technology team and becomes part of the decision-making process, he has greater and newer means to create a new esthetic. Luminaires and other devices, like landscape and paving materials, should be selected for their contribution to coordinated imagery. Housing developments and commercial areas alike can become a new nighttime experience when the scene is defined by regard for people-seeing rather than merely product-making.

Chapter Eight

People on Wheels

The problem with the automobile is that we haven't yet figured out how to get the mechanical monster into the electronic age. Although planners have been long concerned with the strangling of the urban environment by the network of highways and roads, the tightening process continues.

As the traffic jam on downtown streets, at airports, in factory parking lots, and at shopping centers thickens, so does the density of products used for traffic command, control, and communication. These usurp more and more of the sidewalk and airspace over the public right-of-way.

As long as traffic control is approached on a street-corner-by-street-corner basis rather than as a subsystem of city-wide control, we will have confusion. As long as traffic devices of limited capability are continually added to the already jumbled streetscape, we will have chaos. But when traffic-control components and techniques are better related to users and environmental conditions, as eventually they must be, then we will see a most dramatic improvement in the function and appearance of the urban scene.

SOME PROBLEMS

Congestion

In 1907, the horse-drawn vehicle moved through New York City streets at 11.5 miles per hour. In 1966, the average speed of the horseless carriage was 8.5 miles per hour. Abroad the problem is worse. In London 500,000 cars, 8,000 buses, and 6,000 taxis jam the streets every day; average speeds at peak periods are reduced to 2 miles per hour in, say, Old Kent Road.

Uniform control procedures have been developed and made standard over the years to regulate and speed up use of the road. However, there are 30,000 local highway and traffic agencies around the country, each of which may interpret standards in a different manner. Moreover, the standards are related to available products which were obsolete long ago.

Safety

The railroad is laid on a right-of-way placed so as to avoid crossings. Airplanes are separated from each other and people by altitude. Only the city street has no separation of vehicles and pedestrians.

A variety of techniques, devices, and regulations have developed to separate cars from cars and cars from people. Many of the devices and constructions, such as concrete medians and separators, are more hazardous to the driver than his own unrestricted actions.

Although not commonly recognized as such, traffic signals themselves are one of the most dangerous of road hazards. Many traffic engineers agree that traffic lights actually increase rather than decrease accidents. New York State statistics show that accidents at an intersection increase by 48 percent *after* the installation of a red light. Signals are installed at intersections to establish rights-of-way in order to regulate traffic volume. Like some medicines, this cure has unfortunate side effects. The fact that it causes accidental injury and death in significant numbers indicates that many faulty design and installation practices prevail.

Moreover, these products do not really do the job. As traffic counts increase, the proper and safe flow of vehicles becomes more critical and difficult to achieve. To aid efficient movement of traffic with a minimum of conflicts and delays, more traffic lights are installed. However, much programming of signal changes is static and fixed, frozen by a timing pattern based on previous flow. Therefore additional lights are not completely effective; motorists frequently wait for a red-light change at an empty corner. Studies show that this obsolete technique of traffic control may contribute to inefficient use of existing roadways as well as to a frustrating experience for the driver.

Concrete abutment with caution signal, sign, and light "protecting" trolley stop.

Visual Pollution

These traffic products are also the most ugly, numerous, and large-scale of the many urban furnishings in the visual scene.

Many traffic-control devices derive from railroad signals and look it. Present-day controls are still largely made by railroad-equipment manufacturers with large investments in older plant and technology. Although their engineers have achieved high reliability standards over the years, management has been slow to change from bulky electromechanic devices to small solid-state electronic ones. Established procedures impose standards of weight and mass more suited to the mechanical than the electronic age.

A factor leading to sign-product proliferation is the American custom of prohibitory design as a means of conveying instructions. Every city follows the procedure of posting signs along the curb prohibiting this, prohibiting that:

NO LEFT TURN
NO LITTERING
NO PARKING

The number of signs repeating the same admonishment in one block surpasses all sensible needs, and too many signs can be as dangerous as too

Traffic-control clutter on a campus.

Amherst, New York. If at first you don't succeed, try again, and again, and again. . . .

few. Nests of signs, sometimes as many as four and five on one post, challenge the comprehension ability of the most alert motorist. In Buffalo, New York, there are estimated to be 45,000 traffic signs displayed on light standards and makeshift supports. In a typical year, 1966, the city Bureau of Signs and Meters rehabilitated 5,304 traffic signs, fabricated 6,600 new signs, installed 963 concrete foundations, and erected 852 street-name signs. This pattern exists all over the country. Little Rock, Arkansas, established its own traffic-signing shop; in three years the shop brought some 2,000 old signs up to uniform standard and manufactured more than 13,000 new ones. According to a recent study by the Highway Research Board, in the District of Columbia alone there was an inventory of 34,100 parking signs estimated to carry over 51,000 parking messages.

Redundancy

When three, four, five, or ten traffic signals are required at one intersection to let motorists know who has the right-of-way, then it is clear that something is wrong with the design of the signal, the design of the installation, or the design of the intersection. Perhaps all three.

But this kind of design is deliberate. It results from the theory that communicating a message with more than one sign or signal helps minimize the background "noise" of all the competing stimuli on the urban scene. In other words, redundancy is considered desirable.

Although usual engineering practice tolerates some overdesign as a safety factor, redundancy may cause chaos and confusion in the hands of an unskillful engineer. Further, the acceptance of this theory leads to a hardened position that forecloses a number of other options and makes experimental progress much more difficult.

It has been said often enough that between now and the end of the century we must build as many structures as have been built since colonial times. This is possibly true. But it is an extension of colonial thought to suppose that we must therefore double the number of street products.

The theory of redundancy of products as a substitute for more efficient and economical systems design and siting is increasingly suspect. It is clearly evident that many oversignaled intersections are confusing and hazardous. Cities have begun to reject highway designs that carve choice property from city tax rolls or destroy valuable urban imagery. Similarly it is increasingly necessary that traffic-control products be evaluated by performance criteria which look at results achieved in terms of urban systems design objectives.

SYSTEMS COMPONENTS

One of the advantages of federal expenditure for research and development is that some lessons learned the hard and expensive way in one area have

application in another. Progress made in human-engineering research for aerospace has application in public hardware. There should be design fallout.

An area of great potential improvement exists in reanalysis of the problem-solving capability of traffic-control devices. Present information processing and display systems use three components which are very much evident in the environment: detectors, controllers, and signals. How do they work? How can they be improved?

Surveillance: Detectors and Controllers

All-weather, real-time, low-error devices are required to count movements by lane and also to indicate vehicular speed and type. This includes automatic remote reporting. A variety of intelligence can be received, or sensed, by surveillance instruments adapted from military research, such as doppler radar.

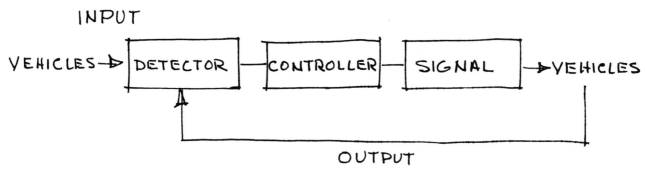

INPUT

VEHICLES → | DETECTOR | — | CONTROLLER | — | SIGNAL | → VEHICLES

OUTPUT

Feedback in a traffic-control system.

Space-age sensing, Victorian ironmongering.

Sensing units such as detectors determine vehicular movement and furnish information input on it to the traffic system. These presence-detection units may be vehicle-actuated by radar, ultrasonic, infrared, pressure-sensitive, magnetic, or other techniques. They may be installed under, over, or at the side of roads, depending upon the principle of operation. To minimize visual pollution, criteria of selection and installation should require miniaturization and integration into existing supports.

After receiving input data on vehicle count from sensing devices, controllers determine appropriate changes in the cycling of the system. They control the movement of vehicles by establishing which particular lane is to go. They may automatically recognize unbalance in opposing traffic and continually adjust the length of go time as the number of vehicles moving on each go signal changes. They can select time intervals as required. They vary the output accordingly in the form of changed signal display. Although the state of the art permits miniaturization of these cast-iron "caskets" which obstruct sidewalks, cities have not yet considered the matter sufficiently important to exert marketplace pressures upon producers.

Vehicle and Pedestrian Signals

The signal head is the display component of the system that the human being must scan. To display a simple go, no-go command, many combinations of colors have been tried:

```
RED    YELLOW   GREEN
GREEN  YELLOW   RED
RED    RED   YELLOW   GREEN
```

The obsolete four-deck configuration was based on the redundancy theory: "two reds are better than one." In delightfully ironic contrast, legal standards for signals have been known to be established and sanctified without benefit of *any* theory. Consider the size and shape of the signal lens. There are two sizes, the newer 12-inch and the traditional 8-inch, which really measures 8⅜ inches. The latter standard was established years ago when a manufacturer who received an order for a signal happened to have available a Corning glass mold measuring 8⅜ inches. Ever since, we have been sitting in our motor cars and staring at *trolley-car* headlamp lenses!

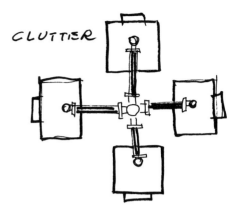

There is a special problem involving pedestrians in all this. Even the most advanced detectors provide data only on presence of vehicles, vehicle volume, and direction of travel. No indication is given of pedestrians. Therefore in areas of heavy foot traffic or at midblock locations manual push buttons may be required as an alternate mode for signal system actuation.

Obviously, more efficient display shapes could be created, given today's awareness of perceptual needs. Possibly a long rectangular display face horizontally mounted across the road would be more effective than vertical stacks of several lenses. Perhaps a round bull's-eye whose single face changed color and symbol would afford more target and recognition value. Further, the frequently employed practice of assembling separate signal decks for each approach should be reexamined. Since the geometry of the intersection does not change, flexibility of arrangement is not always a virtue—particularly if it unnecessarily confuses clarity of statement. The higher cost of additional units is unwarranted. Fixed heads are more compact and less wasteful of space than a cluster of stacks.

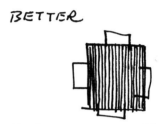

Signal arrangements compared in plan view.

Also, serious consideration should be given to the painted color of the signal array. For years New York State practice was to paint the assembly "traffic yellow." Although this color obviously diminished the contrast and therefore legibility of the yellow light, the practice was not changed until recently, when the California practice of using neutral dark gray was adopted, making the signal colors much more visible.

Other factors such as climate and community identity should also be considered in choosing an equipment color, and where particularly difficult solar conditions exist, for example, where the signal faces east or west, the lens may be sun-shielded by a variety of visor shapes. If the surround or background is cluttered, a neutral panel can be applied to blank out the "noise."

As in all systems relationships, the first inquiry must be, "What are the goals? What purpose is the device to serve?" The purpose of pedestrian signals presently is not to expedite the movement of people, but to limit their passage so as to assign more roadbed time to cars.

This goal results in products which minimize social benefit and encourage killing and injuring people. After several pedestrians were killed at my street corner, I timed the pedestrian signal and found it to offer a WALK indication for eleven seconds. Eleven seconds for an elderly person or child—who else walks?—to cross a busy roadway! Clearly these people would be better off

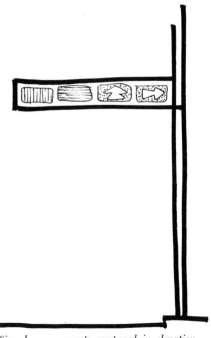

Signal arrangements compared in elevation. Best.

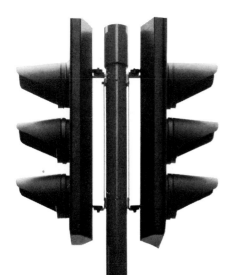

Century City, California. Sheet-metal surround painted flat dark gray does not compete with signal colors, but separates signals from background.

without this product and using their own native judgment in observing traffic conditions.

In addition to reexamination of device function and timing, consideration should be given to the use of symbols rather than legend. To get halfway across a street and see DON'T WALK is confusing and frightening. Far better to use, as in Canada, the sequence of flashing orange-colored hand, constant orange hand, green-colored man walking.

Today more and more cities are reprogramming and computerizing their city-wide traffic-control systems, particularly those controlling movement from high-speed expressways into downtown streets. The future New York City traffic-control system, for example, will include radar sensing of flow at many intersections, with real-time computer adjustment of traffic-light timing within the feedback loop. In Toronto, a large-scale Univac has already been hooked up to take data simultaneously on what ultimately will be a 1,000-intersection system. Detectors report on the passage of all the vehicles

New traffic-signal system for the Ministry of Transport. Molded-plastic signal shells are less obtrusive, costly, heavy.

in the system by scanning them at sixty-four pulses per second, and the data are fed into a central computer. The computer figures out the quantity, speed, and position of the traffic and activates the intersection lights to keep the traffic flowing smoothly.

Signaling systems controlled from a central point are also feasible when the mode of traffic detection is closed-circuit television. Cameras furnishing visual measurements that are interpreted by trained observers are a convenient and economical method of controlling a small system. These control systems are in use at military installations, parking garages, and central business districts. One large installation at Sydney, Australia, employs twelve 16-millimeter TV cameras, remotely controlled from the traffic-control center. Observers, using visual data from the cameras, may vary any established pattern of control. They select appropriate prepared programs for insertion into central control equipment. The programs specify the selection and arrangement of signal time intervals.

These innovative systems configurations will require sophisticated components. Some are already within the state of the art; others are yet to be designed; in each case better rapport must be achieved between people and signals. In the accomplishment, an unparalleled opportunity also exists for improved community pride and identity. This is achieved through consumer-oriented design. Shape that instills confidence. Color that promotes safety. Typeface and graphics that imply precision. Materials that demonstrate awareness. Visibility of message that demonstrates regard for the consumer. Components and installation that work together as coordinated units to demonstrate a feeling of municipal concern for the pedestrian and reassure him. In short, the design must involve the driver or pedestrian in a favorable way and make him want to cooperate.

SIGNS

Legend versus Symbol

At the moment, the city contains a big heap of signs dumped down in a most monotonous and dreary way. The planner-designer, through the technique of system design, must sort out the heap and give it order, pattern, and meaning.

Traffic-sign shapes, colors, symbols, lettering, etc., have been the subject of much research and discussion and many international meetings. The systems most used originated in the United Nations World Conference on Road and Motor Transport held in Geneva in 1949. This proposed a protocol on road signs and signals which could be adopted by those countries wishing to do so pending establishment of a worldwide system. The protocol sign

Experimental cellular traffic signal.

Swiss Pavilion, Lausanne Fair. Protocol sign and symbol exhibit.

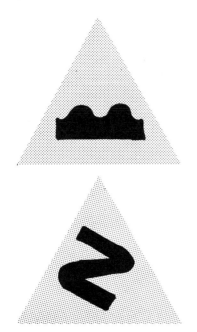

Pictorial symbols for uneven pavement and curve, first conventionalized in Paris, 1926.

system has since been adopted by approximately thirty countries, including most of Europe. The United States and the United Kingdom have not adopted the protocol.

After the 1949 Geneva conference, a group of six experts drawn from six countries, including the United States, attempted to devise a system acceptable to both the New World and the Old. This resulted in a United Nations Draft Convention in 1953. This also has not been accepted in the United States.

In England, the Anderson Committee Final Report of 1960 reflected the work of a professional designer, Jock Kinneir of London. For the first time anywhere "esthetic" and "amenity" considerations were stressed. A major change was adoption of an alphabet of initial capitals, with lowercase designed by Kinneir. Kinneir also developed arrows, which he further refined in the Worboys Committee Report, 1963.

The difference between United States and protocol signs is that the former use mainly words and the latter rely to a great extent on symbols only. United Kingdom practice is to use both symbols and words. In Canada more than 75 percent of the regulatory signs contained in the *Manual on Uniform Traffic Control* were symbolized to minimize the dual-language problem. The *United States Manual on Uniform Traffic Control Devices* is in process of major revision. The "Joint Committee" considered a wider adoption of symbols in preference to word messages as an important step toward greater safety and facilitation of traffic movement and control. In 1969, the Committee approved the use of over thirty symbols standardized by the United Nations, Vienna, 1968 Convention on Road Signs and Symbols.

The systems designer must decide the degree of abstraction to use in signing. There are three general approaches corresponding to three kinds of signs:

Ionic—A sign which has resemblances to things it stands for (picture)
Symbolic—A sign which uses abstracted devices (arrow)
Alphabetical—A sign which uses letters or typography

The dual approach, a common procedure, is questionable since it promotes confusion and reduces message comprehension. The avoidance of use of words with symbols has the advantage that bigger letter forms or symbols, one or the other, can be used without increasing sign size.

The Message

Messages inform us and demand action. The designer must decide when communication with the driver is necessary to aid the safe and orderly movement of traffic. Information must be made apparent on special regulations which apply to specific places under specific conditions. The driver must be warned about hazards which are not self-evident.

Uniformity and consistency of application, standardization of design, and legibility are essential to safe and efficient traffic control. Various criteria for the alphabet, legend, size, and placement of signs are set forth in regulations of state traffic commissions. Within the traffic-communications vocabulary, however, value judgments must still be made. Needs must be determined. Appropriate installations must be designed and sited. The principal criterion should be clarity of command. If the system is poorly designed with frequent and confusing commands, people will ignore or unknowingly violate these orders.

The driver may be warned or directed to take some specific action by a number of instrumentalities classified as regulatory or warning.

Regulatory signs give the driver notice of city traffic laws or regulations that apply to a given place or time. They may be mandatory (do!), such as STOP or SQUEEZE LEFT. Or they may be prohibitory (do not!), such as NO PARKING or DO NOT ENTER.

Warning signs alert the driver to potentially hazardous conditions. Most of these signs reflect road conditions, such as a curve or bump, and have little urban use. However, warning signs whose need arises from the presence of other people, such as schoolchildren, are frequently seen.

United Kingdom traffic-sign alphabet.

Geneva, 1931

Geneva, 1949

Anderson Committee, 1960

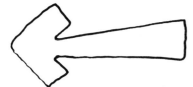

Worboys Committee, 1963

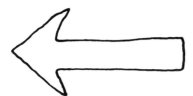

State Traffic Commission

Classic design for road marker which pre-dates Swiss system for organization of many bits of information, Illinois Division of Highways, 1925.

Shape

Clear distinction between regulatory or warning signs and those of guidance or orientation is necessary. The former require action—observance of a regulation or especially careful driving. The latter require no action; the signs are posed as an aid. This distinction in sign media may be achieved by shape, color, and/or message.

As a visual aid to recognition, shapes of signs have been coded to the sign vocabulary. The following shapes have a uniform meaning in all states:

> Octagon—STOP
> Equilateral Triangle (one point down)—YIELD
> Round—RAILROAD CROSSING
> Diamond—Hazard warning
> Rectangular (long dimension vertical)—Regulatory
> Rectangular (long dimension horizontal)—Guide

The full potential of shape as a recognition symbol has not yet been realized. A recent CBS TV presentation of the National Drivers Test revealed that only 25 percent of a national sampling of drivers scored a good or excellent rating. The majority of drivers even failed to identify an octagonal shape as a stop sign. The difficulty may be found to be that geometric sign shapes have been chosen by engineers without adequate regard for perception abilities of people. The United States shapes (and color and messages) may not be as successful as the protocol shapes and symbols. It is likely that no amount of redundancy will offset an inherently faulty premise.

Color

As a further aid to recognition, color coding has been standardized in an attempt to reinforce sign meaning. The following colors have a uniform meaning in all states:

> red, white legend—STOP
> yellow, black legend—Warning messages
> yellow, black legend—YIELD
> white, black legend—Regulatory messages

Current practice tends to reflectorization of almost all signs with reflective materials and delineators. As an alternative, signs may be self-illuminated in color.

MARKINGS

Under mandates of state traffic commissions all cities provide certain information to motorists by use of markings on the roadway. In 1966, the Buffalo, New York, Bureau of Signs and Meters logged 1.5 million linear feet of center and land markings—about 300 miles, covering less than half of the city's

650 miles of streets. The bureau also installed 17,492 feet of crosswalk markings, or about 3.5 miles.

In Little Rock, Arkansas, traffic-paint consumption recently spurted from 150 to 2,000 gallons per year. This provides 200 miles of center and land striping and 600 pedestrian crosswalks. Automated striping machines are now used which, by spraying preheated paint followed by reflective beads, eliminate the manual placement and removal of line-protective cones and thereby reduce costs from 7 to 3.5 cents per linear foot.

These painted lines or graphics on a two-dimensional surface can contribute to the look of the urban fabric. Correctly used, they can order and regulate traffic with a minimum of aboveground clutter of signing and signals. They can convey certain types of information without diverting the driver's attention from the roadway. Design application does, however, require consideration of snow or rain obliteration.

Color

Color codings are now used for pavement markings to signify meaning:

> white—aid to lane definition
> yellow—mandatory no passing or barrier definition

But other colors can also be used to provide a sense of identity to certain districts, such as Downtown, or even to encircle areas of historical heritage and significance.

Color should also be considered as a functional tool for simplifying night driving. Recent experiments reported by the Eno Foundation for Highway Traffic Control suggest the desirability of treating roadway surfaces with a reflective color to provide information. All roadway elements such as lanes, signs, and dividers having a common purpose could be treated in the same color. Blue has not been used for any major highway-traffic function and could be used as the identifying color. This technique could have application where velocities must change, as at arterial intersections with residential streets.

Even greater results can be achieved when texture is used in addition to color. Imbedded aggregates or applied materials can furnish the driver information by feel and sound as well as sight. Three-dimensional surfaces in combination with more advanced visual graphic designs can promote safer and more efficient traffic operations.

SITING

Goggled and gauntleted, sitting high on his horseless carriage, the early driver needed his signs high. Seventy years later the height hasn't changed. Most vertical signal decks are supported over the road, with at least 15 feet

Church Street project. Color-coded traffic signs relate to light standards.

L'Enfant Plaza, Washington, D.C., 1969. Experimental traffic signs coordinated with other street furniture.

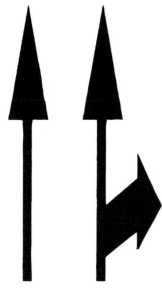

United Nations Conference on Road Traffic, Vienna, December, 1968. Pavement can convey information. Arrow markings in perspective indicate both the direction straight ahead and a turn.

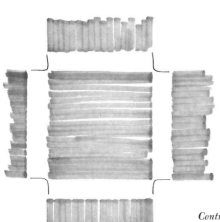

clearance over state highways. Yet the driver needs them lower. His sports-car windshield restricts upward vision from his bucket seat, and he can't see. When stopped for a light, he must crane his head to watch signals, their color is obscured by the sun, swaying from span wires strung between grossly overstated poles.

Clearly, new techniques for siting and support of signs and signals are essential. The most obvious refinements would seem to be integration of the information system into the support system so as to provide a more disciplined presentation at a more useful position relative to the driver.

The layout of sign and signal distribution is still very much an art. Inexpressive and contradictory signs hinder rather than help traffic flow, and may create a hazard. Certainly they create visual clutter. Traffic-control installation plans should be designed for the environment and require the engineer or designer imaginatively to sketch the system configuration in bold strokes, pick the proper products, and put them in the right place. Such a plan will be sensitive to the landscape, respect it, and contribute to the environmental imagery.

Contrasting paving materials provide permanent pedestrian lanes at street intersection.

Chapter Nine

When People Need to Know or Talk

The old neighborhood was a close-knit unit of social relationships and personal contact. When you wanted information on how to get to such and such street, someone was there to tell you. When danger threatened, the group protected its own, or you could run to the corner and call a policeman.

Now there are more people, but there is less assistance. The megastructured city has become depersonalized. With everyone whizzing by on wheels, person-to-person talk is difficult. But more cars produce more accidents or mechanical breakdowns. More aging buildings multiply fire-protection needs. More crime and vandalism on the streets multiply citizen alarm needs.

Under normal circumstances, there is more social and business talk too. Today's teen-ager and businessman alike are affluent and want to have a great deal of communication. Much of this is impulse telephoning in public spaces. Adequate facilities must be provided.

Additionally, in an age of unparalleled literacy, the printed word has less value. An aware population is less responsive to the traditional communications techniques of the municipal establishment. Public signing telling people where to deposit trash, when to stop or go, where to park, is becoming less effective.

The public does want more information: "Where am I? Where do I want to go? How do I get there?" But when the city increases the sign inventory, city streets get more cluttered, and response to the chaotic stimuli diminishes. New information-display techniques of greater clarity and message-carrying capacity are required.

Successful meeting of all these needs can only be accomplished by employing a comprehensive public communications plan utilizing all appropriate media and carefully integrating them with other street facilities. This will also result in an enhanced imagery: in becoming a controlled element of the urban fabric, signage can make a positive contribution to community identity.

PERSON TO PERSON

Public Telephone

People want to talk—they will pay for use of a telephone and even stand and wait in line for the privilege. For example, recent New York Telephone Company studies at the State University of New York at Buffalo campus showed high utilization rates at the Student Union. Twenty-six thousand persons a day entered and left. They were served by only sixteen telephone booths inside, none outside. Lines of waiting patrons were the rule rather than exception.

This small talk adds up to big money. Coin-operated telephones are subject to tariff regulation and are usually known as Public Commission Paying Telephones. This means that the telephone is a vending machine which makes money for the property owner. There are 1,363,000 public booths in the United States, and they are under constant development and redesign for greater consumer satisfaction and better appearance. Changes are also made to incorporate contemporary materials offering improved maintenance and resistance to vandalism.

As a machine selling talk and performing a social need, the public telephone instrument can and should be packaged to contain the necessary components plus optional features geared to the functional, esthetic, and severity-of-use needs of the location. The package may be a complete booth shelter, or it may be a protective and acoustic screen enclosing various components.

Operating components have been engineered for flexibility of installation in a variety of assemblages. Packages can be designed to be used individually or grouped in modular multiples. The designer can choose from a great variety of enclosures or booths, making possible the reinforcement of the particular urban character. The selected configuration can thus make a significant cost-free contribution to imagery and identity.

Distinctive packages can be achieved without complete enclosure of components. In fact, the trend now is to phase out exterior use of the familiar square booth with folding door and even newer models with curved tempered glass, because enclosures present many problems when used outside. Maintenance costs are high. It is difficult to keep booths clean and free of snow, ice, or litter. Booths afford shelter for immoral activities. Booths encourage vandalism, such as cutting of receiver cords and removal of phone housings. Observation of coin-box pilferage is difficult. Above all, telephone booths occupy too much space on the public sidewalk, particularly when used in multiples.

One outdoor model without enclosure, designed by the Bell System with assistance by industrial design consultant Henry Dreyfuss and called "versatel shelves," resulted from a systems approach to solving these problems. Ver-

Familiar orange roof extends corporate image to public telephone.

Dynamic form identifies public telephone at Expo 67, Montreal.

Bell Telephone Laboratories. Four freestanding telephone modules interfaced to stanchion.

F Street Mall, Washington, D.C.

satel shelves have been designed with a pie-shaped configuration (45 degrees) for greater versatility in installation. Up to four units can be arranged kiosk fashion around one post in a space 2 feet 6 inches square, the space required for a single full-size telephone booth. Wiring is concealed in the aluminum-closed structural-steel angle post. Capital requirements and leasing costs are lower. Units can be walk-up types or mounted lower for drive-up. An aluminum sandwich canopy overhangs the walk-up model, providing partial weather protection and additional sound insulation. (This is not necessary or desirable on the drive-up model.) Materials are smooth-surfaced; they clean easily and resist defacing. The stainless-steel coin-collector unit has a redesigned internal mechanism which is almost completely vandal-proof, including those who use cherry-bomb explosives, and the phone cable is steel-covered.

Phone-shelf units such as these can be integrated with other street furniture or into convenience centers such as bus shelters. They are a successful example of urban furnishings that are derived from analysis of environmental and functional needs.

Several factors are considered in deciding on whether or not to provide public telephone facilities and the number of units to be provided. The potential revenue produced by public telephones must be weighed against installation costs tempered by the public convenience factor. Exterior telephones in remote locations require costly trenching and long runs of service and electric cable. Exterior telephones are used less under conditions of cold or inclement weather. Good visibility is required for more frequent use and less vandalism. But more and more frequently the decision is made to install public telephones in all but the most formal outdoor public spaces.

Since all wiring should be underground, one of the important considerations in siting becomes the feed system. Planning for telephone lines should be done in context with other electric service and adjacent utilities. Sharing of costs of trenching and paving by all systems reduces installation costs.

HELP!

Fire

Turning in an alarm by running to the nearest fire-alarm box and pulling the handle is the oldest automated way for a public-spirited person to notify the authorities of a fire. It is also a current mode of leisure-time activity for those who like to play machines and hear fire bells and sirens. In 1967 alone, 48,000 false alarms were turned in in metropolitan New York, and 3,000 alarms were pulled during a seven-hour student rebellion in Paris. In Buffalo, the 1967 total of 3,400 jumped to 5,200 one year later and cost over $100 for each false alarm response.

Fire-alarm equipment is nondiscriminating, single-channel, and without feedback. Whether false or not, the alarm is conveyed in the following manner. Any number of input devices—manually operated pull boxes, automatic sprinklers or fire detectors—can initiate a telegraph signal. The message provided by the signal box is single-purpose (fire protection) and coded (automatic identification of location). The signal is received by a master fire-alarm box, which automatically transmits it directly to the fire department for response to the emergency.

All this equipment is usually not leased as are telephones, but city-owned and -maintained. The location of input stations (fire-alarm boxes) along the public right-of-way is rather arbitrary and based on the estimated number of units required to minimize elapsed reporting time. Cincinnati, for example, has 1,549 fire-alarm terminal heads, using 5,880 conductor-miles of underground and aerial cable.

The tendency now is to use fewer boxes in residential areas, since most fire reporting is by private telephone. But in public areas boxes should be located in convenient and accessible positions of high visibility and left unlocked. For protection of major buildings they should be within line of sight of main exits. In order to reduce the fire hazard to circuit wires, mounting should be freestanding with all wires underground, rather than by attachment to a building.

Although sometimes touted as a piece of Americana, the Victorian alarm box never really aroused much esteem or nostalgia, and remains, simply, some archaic-looking junk on an ornate pedestal. In fact its appearance seems to invite ridicule and vandalism. The legend on many a box instructs the reader to BREAK GLASS. Youngsters do. The door cavities are filled with trash and glass shards. Jagged edges await the wrist veins of any citizen rash enough to reach into the box for the alarm handle during an emergency.

Ironically, this archaic appearance results not from happenstance, but by deliberate design. Although an inner stainless-steel or aluminum box houses electric circuits, the industry has tended to perpetuate the "cottage shape." The rationale for housing automation within an old-fashioned "cottage" is the very incongruity of appearance. The assumption is made that an archaic identity of such strangeness will aid public recognition of the device. Also, the past practice of painting the outer shell "signal red" for greater visibility has been continued. This simplistic practice requires reexamination. Very likely recognition and identity will be better secured by contrast of color and pattern than by uniformity.

The fire-alarm box really should be eliminated by merging its function into the emergency telephone system, but at the very least the environmental designer can effect considerable visual improvement in its siting and method of support. The typical cast-iron pedestal can frequently be deleted by uti-

lizing an existing nearby support in a multipurpose systems-sharing capacity. The multipurpose post could be given visual prominence by means of dynamic striping or color patterns. And the potential of nighttime marker lights should be exploited in shape, placement, or color.

In short, since by definition the fire alarm must be both accessible and properly used, design improvement in shape, color, and mounting is needed to promote recognition characteristics and respectful acceptance by the public.

Emergency-reporting Telephone System

Back in the days of the foot patrolman, a locked iron cabinet containing a telephone was essential for his emergency use and routine check-in. Then the "flatfoot" was made more mobile with wheels and equipped with sophisticated two-way radio which diminished the importance of the police call box as a communications tool. Now there is renewed interest in the telephone call box, which permits police or private citizens to report emergencies of any kind by voice transmission.

Although they have only recently been made available, there are already more than 200 public emergency systems leased from local telephone companies in the United States. Buffalo, New York, as a typical example, installed 467 units in 1967. Each is pedestal-mounted and, although the support is sometimes shared with a fire-alarm box, always has its own circuit. Unfortunately, little public use is made of these emergency telephones even though they are left unlocked, perhaps because the marking POLICE on the instrument conveys the notion they are locked or for police use only. Much more effective utilization would be made if the instrument were designed and identified as a public EMERGENCY system.

The great potential of the emergency telephone system for assuming new tasks is exemplified by new applications such as trouble reporting along expressways. Example: emergency telephones located at half-mile intervals along Interstate 87 (Albany, New York) reduce the labor costs of twenty-four-hour police or service-vehicle patrol.

Community Emergency Communications Center

The most efficient and economical way to receive such telephone input may be to establish a central communications center. In such an urban protection office an illuminated panelboard could serve as combined terminal point, recording instrument, and processing station for all low-voltage alarm devices and radio and telephone emergency communications. Through a console appropriately located in the dispatchers' center, incoming calls could be relayed to the appropriate local fire station, police station, or hospital or ambulance service. This office should be manned twenty-four hours a day and incorporate a "dead-man feature," whereby in case of lack of response to an alarm signal, the alarm would be "remoted" to the nearest fire or police station.

The planner of space, facilities, and services is necessarily involved in communications systems decision making. Careful design and location of exterior equipments should produce more useful communications systems featuring components better adapted to user needs. In fact, in view of the urgent need for improved communications between the public and the authorities, it seems reasonable to introduce use of picture phones. Such image-viewing equipment has been demonstrated frequently by the telephone companies. Technically, service could be made available now over existing circuits simply by modifying telephone switching equipment. Functionally, the initial equipment could be simplified by using fixed camera focus and making the viewing screen available only at the receiving switchboard. The system capability could be extended by the addition of picture-taking capability to the viewing camera, which might reduce the incidence of false-alarm reporting.

PUBLIC SIGNS

Public Nuisance

Ugly, confusing, obsolete public signing has been fodder for years for funny-paper jokes, satirical magazine covers, and serious editorials, yet change in traffic regulation, parking signing, transit information, and route marking is frustratingly slow. Even though simple low-cost improvements could have significant favorable impact on the public, meaningful experiments are rare.

The esthetic sign designs shown each year in graphics books almost invariably are product solutions to private building-identification needs and seldom information systems solutions to public signing needs. Such typographical niceties, no matter how handsome and delicious, do not make the city more viable or intelligible. A more organized wide-scope approach is required by bureaucracy and industry. In a nation of drivers most of us get lost: "What place is this? Where am I going? How do I get there?" The problem: too many places to go, too many ways to get there, too many people, not enough time, too many signs to look at. The sign has replaced the cop at the corner but does not serve as well. The sign remains silent and static and does not solve our problem. Public signing is not an infor-

Primitive but effective sign matrix.

mation system; it is a lash-up grown by accretion. Monostructural systems must take the place of discrete elements.

The Black-Box Bit

The sign painter has outlasted the lamplighter, but is on the way out. Existing sign techniques are inadequate in two major respects: not enough information is given, and there are too many signs for comprehension. Thus the message capacity of conventional signs is limited at a time when information needs increase.

For a time the designer's hope was symbolization. The Brookfield Zoo in Illinois pioneered the use of informal cutout animal symbols instead of complex legends. The Maryvale Shopping Center in Phoenix adopted turtles and alligators five times larger to distinguish zones in the parking lot. Now the designer of every outdoor spectacle feels impelled to use abstract pictographs rather than message sets.

These can be helpful; they may also create greater confusion in understanding than a simple legend. Better comprehension will develop from use of electronic media to meet circulation and information needs. Automated displays offer greater potential for leading one through the expressway maze, along the appropriate arterial, thence to the neighborhood, and finally to the desired local street and parking place.

These information channels are being tried. The Federal Highway Administration, for example, is experimenting with induction radio, triggered prerecorded audio messages, and visual displays on the vehicle controlled by external signals. And considerable potential for information presentation exists in the new science of holography based on optics.

Whatever the media selected, it now seems possible to look at men and automatic machines in interrelationship as information processing systems. In designing such a man-machine configuration, there might be three components:

> An input—The selection of a particular message at a given place or moment in time
>
> A process—The addition of this message to all previous messages that have been selected
>
> An output—a sequential selection of yes or no, go or no go, that is unique

Clearly the operational success of such a system depends on programming and translating data into inputs (language) which are acceptable and meaningful to the processor (human being or machine) and which can reasonably be transformed into useful output (action result). The public agency (transmitter) has a number of purposeful messages to be conveyed or communicated through media (carriers). These messages must first be encoded in a form the human observer (receiver) can understand.

"TURN ME ON"_____ ⊡⊡

HAMLET_____"to be or not to be"

COMPUTER LANGUAGE_____0—1

COMIC BOOK_____ (YES) (NO)

ARISTOTLE_____either—or

BIOLOGY_____ ♀ ♂

LIGHT GLOBE_____ ♀ ♂

SILVER CHLORIDE ON FILM_ ◼ ◻

AVIATION_____flaps up—flaps down

ASTRONAUTS_____go—no go

CRAP TABLE_____come—no come

CHARTIST_____x, y

CHESS_____P-K4, P-Q3

It's a Barnum and Binary World
Just as ideatic as it can be,
But it would only be make-believe
If it wasn't for you and me.

Such messages must be uniformly displayed throughout the city. Messages should be simplified. Parking information, for example, must be presented on a city-block basis rather than store-frontage or foot-by-foot basis. Similar instructions must not be conveyed by different legends. The reinforcement techniques of classical psychology apply: if we wish uniform response, we must apply identical stimulus. Also the configuration of a word, or its "gestalt strength," plays an important part in perception. As in the new mathematics, we must deal with "sets" of symbols or images. We must recognize group effects. The format, or man-machine language, should be of wide application and adaptability that best satisfies human-component needs. The criteria of evaluation is not merely legibility, but *digestibility*.

To read these messages, the brain uses only dots, the number of which per second conveys all information. This is called "pulse-frequency modulation." It is the precursor of, and in many ways resembles, the work computing machines do with electric impulses, positive or negative. The physical world seems to be a yes-no universe. In practical terms messages can be a structured sequence of the dot-and-dash telegraph key, the on-off traffic light, the hole or no hole in a parking-lot pass card. Clearly, the simpler the message within a structure of yes-no choices, the better.

Pictographs, Tokyo Olympics, 1964. The name of the game is pictograph. How many can you identify?

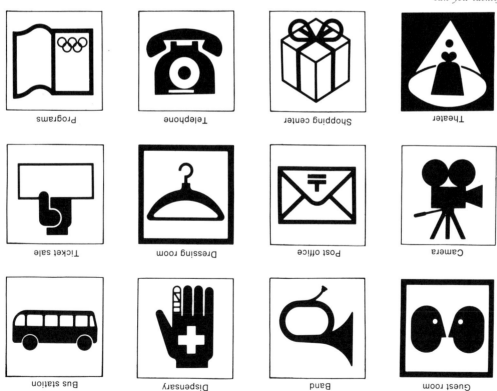

Programs	Telephone	Shopping center	Theater
Ticket sale	Dressing room	Post office	Camera
Bus station	Dispensary	Band	Guest room

Czech Pavilion, Expo 67, Montreal. Push-pull, on-off, variable-media matrix.

An essential component of the information system configuration is the message carrier. The carrier channel for a message need not be a conventional sign panel, but can be streets, curbs, walls, the sky. Whatever the choice, it is desirable that the display be capable of organizing a number of messages. In fact the most economical, space-saving, and versatile carriers will likely be those matrices that are variable and multichannel.

Program Elements

The greatest information systems successes to date have been in transportation, where the professional designer has sometimes worked for an aware public agency willing and able to implement the facility information system. The Montreal subway and several airports in America and abroad exemplify the results to be achieved when users' information needs are considered throughout the program planning and construction and not merely stuck on after the facility is complete. Such successful results with complex transportation facilities are almost invariably the product of disciplined design and management procedures.

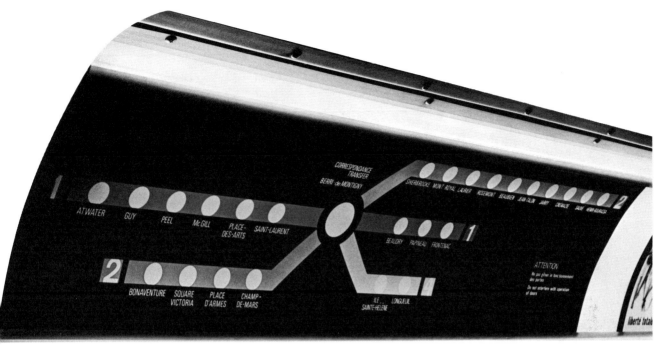

Map, Montreal subway.

West London Air Terminal.

not

When planning the information system for an airport, campus, shopping center, or entire city, four steps must be taken prior to hardware development: problem formulation, data collection, data analysis, design solution. To take these steps properly requires preparation of documents on the following:

Schematic Concept   The appropriate information scheme which best meets the unique communications requirements is visualized and presented in context with the specific environment.

Siting Plan and Schedule   The availability and sequence of information to the observer are shown on site drawings. All information, orientation, and control elements for motorist and pedestrian are precisely defined, located, and keyed to a list of carefully considered and authorized legends.

Component Specifications   The procurement drawings and descriptions of all elements which comprise the information-display system are gathered together. Included are specifications for panels, supports, typography, color, and other standardized components.

Sign Standards   A manual detailing the operating procedures and standards mandatory with administrative and shop personnel for consistent application of the system is prepared. This maintains the integrity of the original concept and assures uniform solutions.

SIGN SYSTEM COMPONENTS

Surround

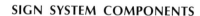

but

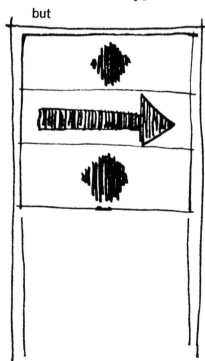

The sign painter's period being past, the designer is less and less concerned with the gestural sign shape or idiosyncrasy of typography and more and more with the ordering device. This tends to be composed of panel modules which can be assembled in varying combinations and organized and positioned by a support matrix.

Whatever its form, the device derives from societal behavior and the industrial process. The surface of the data-display panel should be made uniform and innocuous. Because people are under continuous bombardment of stimuli, designers must eliminate unnecessary background or extraneous conditions detrimental to the central purpose. The designer first determines what is most relevant, then screens out the background "visual noise" that degrades the signal and destroys message comprehension.

In addition, the display system itself should have inherent flexibility, for change and expansion. It is a good rule not to chisel a name on a building. Nothing is permanent, not even a bank name or a college hall or a one-way-street designation.

And finally, the matrix system with plug-in panels imposes discipline where a number of competing messages must be accommodated simultaneously in a limited space. Such a system can tolerate and even enhance differentiation of message between, say, traffic-control and parking information subsystems, by use of controlled family relationships of position, size, color, or texture. Such a family of color relationships for road signs was successfully developed by Jock Kinneir, consultant designer to the Road Research Laboratory in England. The panel color code was:

Motorways	Blue
A Through Routes	Green
B Routes	White
Local Streets	White with Blue Border

Alphabet

When considering legibility, other aspects besides content are concerned. Once the need for comprehensibility of message has been satisfied, the selection of typography for better legibility begins. Here size and shape of letter form, line width, and spacing between lines are involved. Beyond legibility, enhancement of the environment or of community identity partly depends upon choice of alphabet as well as development of sign surround and support. The letter form becomes part of the urban design vocabulary.

A readily available typeface should be selected or modified for standardized use for all city needs. Since different departments have different tasks requiring different emphasis, an alphabet offering a family of options (bold, italic, regular) may be advisable.

The technique of graphic design has been detailed in other books, but it might well be noted here that, as in corporate identity programs, the designer's choice of typeface is instrumental in expressing the public posture of the sponsoring agency. The selected alphabet can make the city or department appear naïve or knowledgeable, traditional or progressive, pompous or helpful.

Linear lettering casts linear shadows over linear wall pattern. Unreadable moiré.

Example: Parking Garage

Task: Develop a guidance system for staff and visitors using the parking facility of the Downstate Medical Center, State University of New York. The structure contains nine levels, none of which are horizontal. The site is in Brooklyn, New York.

Problem: Two parts: First, the facility has a confusingly great number of entrances, some restricted to staff. Second, the constant change of floor levels makes it difficult for a user to find his parked vehicle.

Analysis: First, it is necessary to provide identification of entrances and direction of travel—up and down, in and out. Second, there must be a constant visual cue to user's elevation.

Synthesis: Develop a concept that provides orientation information to user in four modes:

1. Legend coding of entrances
2. Numerical coding of floor levels
3. Color coding of floor levels
4. Pictorial presentation of user elevation above or below grade by means of "thermometer" concept

Downstate Medical Center, State University of New York. (Above) Orange porcelain, enamel and steel marker for parking garage. (Below) Horizontal color bar shifts up or down, cuing user to position in parking garage.

Chapter Ten

Good Housekeeping
and the Good Life

Yesterday's luxury is today's necessity. The sparse rigors of Puritan living have long since lost attraction or even justification in an economy capable of producing endless conveniences and comforts.

Technology and industry have made available to the average homeowner a host of laborsaving appliances and leisure-enjoyment equipments. The public environment is an extension of the consumer's home and other private spaces. The standards of one must echo the standards of the other. Is the public willing to leave the climate-controlled environment of home or office to stand on a cold, wet street and wait for a bus? Failure to provide ordinary convenience has contributed to poor acceptance and economic failure of many mass-transportation systems. So it is with many aspects of our graceless cities.

Designers and industry have the challenge and opportunity to create new services and machines of attractive visual character that will make the city more pleasurable and habitable. What is required is the imaginative analysis of both environmental needs and peoples' wants, then their design articulation.

KEEP THE RAIN OFF

Kiosks

As Halprin pointed out, "kiosk" comes from the old Turkish word "kiūsch" and means "pavilion." The term and use have crept into our vernacular, and we tend to think favorably of the handsome Parisian structures covered with colorful collage.

Kiosks are particularly well suited to the leisurely European scene of plazas, open spaces, and broad walks, but have not transplanted well to the hustle-bustle of contemporary America. Still, street shelters are needed. They are needed not only as public bulletin board, street directory, newsstand, post office, or whatever, but also as dynamic punctuation and relief from the gray monotony of the streetscape. And since visibility to attract users and addition of color and gaiety to the street are compatible, clearly they should be designed with a sense of drama and flair.

Microarchitecture frequently produces more clutter than imagery.

Santa Monica Mall, California.

Bus Shelters

Transit companies often are still privately owned, but their routes and stops are publicly controlled, and the degree of service they provide at stops is of public concern. Considerations of service here include not only the length of waiting time but also the degree of protection and comfort provided the patron on the street. The trend now is to provide shelters, particularly at those locations where installation is obviously warranted by density of use.

In the past, few criteria have been available to the designer to help determine the extent of enclosure, area required per waiting patron, width/length ratio of floor plan, or need for amenities such as seating, route information, entertainment, and litter collection. Therefore bus shelters have tended to be site-built architectural features and frequently have been more affluence symbol than shelter. More recently, the trend has been to product design. But the concept remains architectural: curtain-wall building off-site-fabricated and on-site-erected, conventional framing with infilling of sandwich panels or glazing. When industry recognizes the market, however, then most certainly the next generation of street shelters will emerge as low-cost, mass-produced monostructures.

Magdalen Street, Norwich, England. Bus-stop shelter.

"Unit system shelter."

THE EFFLUENT SOCIETY

Litter-collection System

The disposable package is the symbol of the American economy. Americans produce a colossal amount of garbage and trash, an average of 4.5 pounds per capita per day not counting sewage. And a study of public disposal habits confirms that people will throw away on public sidewalks umbrellas, newspapers, beer cans, and almost anything else you can name. During an academic year, ten thousand students on a campus will throw away a million chewing-gum wrappers, candy cartons, and cigarette packs. The United States discards 440,000 tons of rubbish every day—an amount which has increased 60 percent since 1950, twice the rate of the United States population increase. The national cost of refuse disposal has reached $3 billion. Half of this is paid by municipalities, the rest by private consumers and commercial establishments. With every forecast of the packaging industry for increased sales, one can assume that the disposal problem will multiply correspondingly.

Many communities are increasing incinerator or dumping facilities. New emphasis is being placed on more efficient housekeeping procedures. More efficient materials-handling techniques are desirable. The container is the first component of the collection system, the one in direct relationship to man. Clearly, its manner and degree of use affect the complete system and warrant detailed study and design.

Criteria

Many communities still fail to provide public trash receptacles. Others provide receptacles that look as if they were made in a boiler factory. In these communities the product is considered a necessary evil, somewhat like a toilet, to be hidden away and used as inconspicuously as possible. Inevitably such a product will be designed in a superficial manner. It will repel the consumer who should be encouraged to use it. Or, conversely, the sanitation department may make an issue of litter control, threaten the public with monstrous fines, and, in so doing, encourage resistance or vandalism. Or occasionally the Downtown Businessmen's Association will act as prime mover in compelling the city to procure new off-the-shelf containers. Because these products are readily available and inexpensive relative to other street improvements, they seem a quick means of sprucing up Downtown for an impending fair, convention, or other event attracting many visitors. Unfortunately these products seldom match in color, shape, or scale other public products in the cityscape. The cosmetic freshening of Main Street fails to hide more serious blemishes. The new look is not really new and soon fades into obscurity.

Public trash receptacles must be seen to be used. But they must appear modest and utilitarian. Design or selection of containers must be based on performance criteria. The standards should derive from public refuse needs and the city's procedures for collection and disposal.

Frequently, public health authorities provide the impetus for a new or more critical analysis of these procedures. National standards of refuse control and collection are rising. Previously acceptable practices of burning trash and garbage in open containers such as those formerly used in Boston Common are now not tolerated. Even the boy scouts are no longer permitted by county health departments to burn refuse in open parkland, but must use disposable paper bags. So that the disposable inner liner has joined the two other acceptable modes of trash removal from receptacle, the self-dumping unit with hinged bottom or side and the inner container which is removed, dumped, and replaced.

But whatever the technique or procedure followed, the refuse-collection system will be successful only to the extent that the containers are used by the people. Greater utilization will be secured by, first, determination of the best receptacle locations, and second, choice of appropriate receptacle size and shape.

Siting

Enough trash receptacles (or litter bins) should be provided to be immediately visual and available. Sparse siting outdoors will be self-defeating. Units should be available near major path intersections. Receptacles should be placed near benches and be made available in areas of rest and recreation. On city streets, the usual procedure is to put out additional units on request for thirty-day trial. The city of Cincinnati, employing this procedure, usually maintains 600 units throughout the city.

Container

Studies or published standards validating optimum volumes for receptacles are not yet available, but the necessary capacity will depend on the ratio of desired frequency of removal to rate of use as determined by city agencies. The desired container volume can be secured with an infinite number of valid shapes varying from geometric to quite plastic. A suitable configuration might result from consideration of the performance criteria. Shape would be influenced by such factors as means of litter removal (liner, container, self-dump), installation technique (floor, wall, post), degree of weather protection and odor containment desired, and choice of material and industrial process.

Fresno Mall, California.

As can be seen on the city street, almost every material has been used for the outer container: cast concrete, fabricated steel, perforated or molded plastic. Each can work well. Perhaps the choice of material should derive not only from criteria of use and shape but also from compatibility with other components of the environment.

WATER TO PUT OUT FIRES WITH

Two Martians land on Earth. One walks up to a fire hydrant and says, "Take me to your leader." The other Martian says, "What are you talking to him for? He's only a kid."

This old joke has its point: the average fire hydrant is very noticeable on the sidewalk and does look like a mechanistic little out-of-this-world creature. Actually, the hydrant is nothing more than a water faucet which can be located anywhere along a pipeline and has a simple mechanism to turn on or off the flow of water. But as a piece of public plumbing, it needs analysis and design.

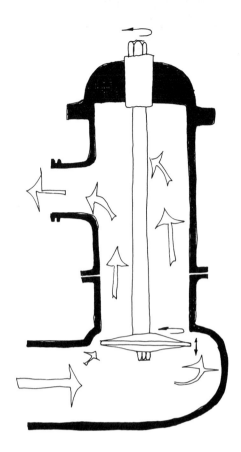

Early hydrants were primitive mechanical faucets with complicated and exposed valve linkage. Some are still in use. In Boston they have been enclosed in pressed-steel housings, and in Toronto cosmetic stainless-steel jackets have been applied. The concern here, however, is with the more recent hydrants in the public right-of-way, which are functionally classified in three types: wet barrel, dry barrel, and vault. The dry barrel has been preferred in the snow belt, where freezing conditions may prevail. In the recessed vault mode all operating mechanisms and hose connections are compactly enclosed in a covered cast-iron box installed flush with grade. Although the vault is not commonly used along roads, where snowplow burial or icing may render the unit invisible or inoperative, it can work well on a well-maintained plaza, street, or sidewalk.

The operating procedure is so simple small boys on hot city streets soon learn how. At the top a readily accessible large turning nut of any shape connects to and turns a plug (compression valve) which screws down into an elbow at the bottom. Then the water gushes up the barrel out of the elbow charged by the pipeline. To shut off the water, the stem nut is turned, the valve rises, and water pressure helps the valve seal the opening.

Flow measurement is the usual rating method for hydrants, which are classified according to capacity: class A, 1,000 gallons per minute or greater; B, 500 to 1,000 gallons per minute; C, less than 500 gallons per minute. Functional criteria have been developed by the American Water Works Association, and new products may be tested and standards evolved at the Underwriters Laboratories at Chicago.

Color has an important bearing upon the hydrant's obtrusiveness in the

Fresno Mall, California.

visual scene. Some cities use a gray neutral color for the barrel in order to "paint out" the object. Some private developers paint hydrants in "corporate" colors, such as purple in the wine-making district of central New York or turquoise and orange in front of Howard Johnson's restaurants. However, many communities color-code hydrant capacity and paint the tops as follows: class A, green; B, orange; and C, red.

Material for hydrants may be cast iron because weight is not a critical factor; durability, resistance to water pressure, and vandalism are. The iron barrel should be of fail-safe construction with a shear device. Breakaway design permits the upper part of the unit to be carried away on impact without injury to the motorist or loss of water pressure.

Scale concerns the apparent size of the hydrant in relation to its surroundings. Customarily the hydrant has been decorated rather than designed, with dimensions and shapes arbitrary. Recent West Coast designs have shown that sculptural shapes can be modeled to use little sidewalk space and be less obtrusive and more handsome. The next steps in hydrant design may be in the direction of miniaturization and greater coordination with other urban furnishings in siting, shape, and color.

Santa Monica Mall, California.

Chapter Eleven

Pride, Pomp, and Planter

In earlier times, even the meanest, dreariest crossroads hamlet was likely to have one grass square or traffic circle complete with granite-faced heroic figure and commemorative plaque, and this tombstone sculpture provided a sense of place. Or the public space may have been made musical by the sound of birds in a park or water from a fountain. Whatever the medium of accent was, you knew where you were and remembered where you had been.

Regardless of technological change, human needs remain the same. And when the city dweller has been provided the basic necessities, the furnishing of the city is not yet done. There remains the desire for an extra treat, an extravaganza, some touch of excitement to put pleasure in urban living.

Today, it's hard to find. Whether to visit or live in, many American cities are dull places indeed. Older neighborhoods are blighted and dying. Newer housing developments are at best bland and "solid." Blocks of new prime-rental office buildings such as those on Third or even Park Avenue in New York are monstrously monotonous. Large sections of the city have lost character and become gray and dispirited. Something is missing.

Color it green. Spark it red or orange. Make it sing or scream, but don't let it whimper.

WHERE YOU ARE
AND WHERE YOU'VE BEEN

Landmarks

When the commercial street, shopping plaza, or mall wants to identify its merchant area as different from all others, then memorable visual attractions are installed which offer inspirational or entertainment value. In fact, the art of producing a community attraction, like show business, is the art of touching people in some emotional way.

But what audience response is desired? Which particular character of the public place is to be enhanced? How much imagery is to be achieved? At what cost, paid by whom? The decision to entertain or move or inspire people requires precise definition of goals, constraints, and resources before seeking solutions. Only then can appropriate devices such as landmarks be developed which produce instant recognition, identification, excitement. At the same time, if worth is shallow, instant appeal may be followed by instant dismissal. It may be necessary for imagery to appear timeless and permanent as well as unique to a place.

From these criteria may come the opportunity to utilize something that already exists in the public space. One of the most spectactular European landmarks, Le Jet d'Eau de Genève in the middle of Lake Leman, sprays water

Northland Center, Detroit, Michigan. A landmark in imagery as well as graphics programming.

425 feet into the air. It was originally created to help equalize pressure changes in Geneva's water supply. Each imitation such as the smaller jet in the lake at Reston, Virginia, or the one in the Potomac River at Washington becomes more contrived and therefore less effective.

In small communities a common approach is to rehabilitate and dramatically light an old building of historical interest. Or an old memorial square or traffic circle can be freshly landscaped. But in many smaller communities the sole significant landmark is a church spire, a water tank, or a red-brick factory chimney. Then existing landmarks may need to be supplemented or supplanted because of obsolescence or because a more vital and appropriate identity is desired.

The large city has an intense competitive pressure to assert its importance, wealth, and vitality to the world at large. And its neighborhoods may each in turn require either an expression of economic health and desirability or a focal point around which to build community loyalty.

For any community, large or small, the expression of a contemporary identity could well be based on technological phenomena. In the past the most successful landmarks have been those structures which reflected unique or daring exploitation of new technical processes. The outstanding successes have been those which additionally enticed observer participation or involvement. And the mode of expression, depending upon the wealth and sophistication of the city, has ranged from revenue-producing utilitarian structures to huge playthings selling only *joie de vivre*. Examples: a bridge of daring engineering whose largeness of concept captures the public imagination; a sports stadium whose bulk and glittering dome are visible along a waterfront or mark an expressway interchange; a needle-shaped observation tower whose lofty rotating restaurant serves as a homing beacon.

Even more advanced techniques based on emotionally involving the observer with some form of contemporary technological experience are useful today. In fact, luminokinetic artists go so far in creation of landmarks as to work toward the total disappearance of the structure in the production of direct *effects*.

Derived from the kinetic art experiments of Duchamp, Man Ray, Gabo, and Moholy-Nagy and utilizing new techniques such as cybernetics, spectacular huge constructions and spatiodynamic towers are now associated with town planning. The resultant landmarks appear to be expressions of the contemporary environment. Designers such as Heinz Mack of Germany's experimental Group Zero and Nicholas Schöffer work in an elegant techno-scientific mode. Content is abandoned for the purely perceptual. At night multi-image moving projections transform the outdoors into a cinema nightscape. The dynamic effects are dazzling and supercharged; the sum of light and motion is more powerful than the parts.

The Mall, Fresno, California, 1964. Clock initially criticized for poor legibility, but now accepted and liked as total sculpture.

Triangular stressed-skin structure contains train of passenger cars traveling within to observation platform at top.

Cybernetic Tower, higher than the Eiffel Tower, functions as esthetic "governor" of Paris. Its luminokinetic elements include over 3,000 multicolored projectors, 2,000 electronic flashlights, 330 mirrors. Acting on data received from hygrometers, thermometers, anemometers, microphones, and photoelectric cells, a central computer constantly changes the rhythm of the elements to represent the esthetic condition of the city.

From Hero on Horseback to Nude with Hole in the Head

In Renaissance times human sculpture, often nude, in an Italian town center might identify the community or reinforce its image. For the time and place in history such sculpture made sense and was appropriate. The Italian city had a tradition of nude gods and goddesses; sculptors and marble were plentiful.

The tradition of representational sculpture was transplanted to America. National leaders were sculpted in togas or fig leaves. Military men were put astride rearing bronze beasts to kindle awe and respect in the breast of the local citizenry.

Representational sculptures of great men installed in public places symbolized the aspirations of growing cities; but the transplanted tradition did not always take root, and there was controversy. In 1783 Horatio Greenough carved a statue of Washington in marble for the Washington D.C., Mall which was rejected by the public, whose common sense could not accept the general of Valley Forge shown as a half-naked Greek god. The next try at memorializing George Washington was Robert Mills's design, an obelisk rising out of a colonnaded Greek temple. It was not built for lack of money for one hundred years; the obelisk part only was completed in 1884. This is the Washington Monument, now the American people's favorite "sculpture."

Today the need for symbolization and identification still exists. It exists in the corporate city, where boxy office skyscrapers raised on pilotis or stuck to the ground occupy a complete block and need something to announce the front entrance, and it exists in the civic or cultural center, whose pedestrian spaces seem to require art to look at.

Current practice for office skyscrapers is just to install a smaller complementary version of the building, a cube, say, which does not compete with the architecture. But today no first-class cultural center is complete without its Picasso, Calder, or Moore. The avant-garde pioneers of thirty years ago are now accepted as masters of middle-class modern. Unfortunately however, many of their selected or commissioned urban art works are still studio conceptions. They are overscaled and violate rather than adorn the urban environment. To these masters of the studio language the language of the streets is alien. When they speak, they only add to the general noise and confusion. Their image is not necessarily transferable. The space may only be decorated, not identified favorably to the consumer.

This view of the corporate and cultural sculptural scene becomes important when we turn to the public sector and note that it is now permissible to spend money for art in urban renewal or new town building. It is all right to budget 1 percent of project cost for amenities such as sculpture or fountains. For example, 5 million of the 480 million dollars put into the South Mall State Office Complex in Albany, New York was budgeted for art.

With government acceptance of art as a desirable and a project-reimbursable item comes the opportunity for employing these funds to secure greater entertainment and recreational value rather than mere adornment. Presently there is a prevailing emphasis on monumental and "conversational" sculpture. This Renaissance concept is expressed in welded steel rather than cast bronze, but remains static in concept. In the public space the designer might better provide a dynamic spatial experience. The user can be encouraged to enter, feel, sense a shape growing from the floor. He can be enveloped in a daytime environment of supergraphics. He can be given a nighttime environment of changing light and color whose programmed automated display excites and delights.

Lincoln Center, New York. Monumental, impersonal, "don't touch."

Expo 67, Montreal. Public art for people,
not "experts."

Whether such public art is good or bad is immaterial. What counts is that it be accessible and not boring. It should be evocative rather than representational, humorous rather than pompous, imaginative rather than literary; and to be truly useful, it should be not merely decorative but inviting of public participation.

WATER TO WATCH AND HEAR

Like the flickering magic of fire, the wonder of water has always stimulated emotional response from man, and time and technology have not changed this natural response. In the country he never tires of watching and listening to water swirl in pools, leap over falls, crash on rocks. In his home, life-giving water offers him sensory satisfaction as he drinks or bathes. The visual and musical qualities of water can similarly stimulate people in the urban public space. They will play in it, eat in it, make music in it, use it as their urban source of refreshment. For, with increasing emphasis on conformance to

Reston, Virginia. Public art of human scale
meant to be enjoyed.

224

codes, cost control, and quantification, water remains a commodity which can be not only essential but frivolous, playful, and organic, meeting human psychological needs in the synthetic city.

Clearly, then, the city dweller needs, wants, will pay for, and should have water integral to his environment. But clearer understanding of public needs and better definition of goals are required to achieve a useful and at the same time appropriate water product. Frequently, as things stand, the designer's client (the city) presents the product, and then the real client (the public) uses it in an unexpected, need-fulfilling way. Then comes outrage. Consider a typical reaction. The *Washington Post* recently reported in great detail that "Alexandria's City fathers made it a crime last night for anyone to play in a reflecting pool at City Hall. . . . [The city attorney] solemnly explained that violaters would be subject to fines and jail sentences of up to six months. . . . the 75 foot square reflecting pool, which contains seven fountains, has proved an attraction to many children. . . . The fountain is the central feature of the plaza, which cost $1.6 million and was built with urban renewal funds."

Every age has its ideals and needs and develops the technology to accommodate them. In Roman times precise, practical engineering brought water over the hills in aqueducts which provided an expression more bold and beautiful than the dispensing fountains themselves. In Renaissance times the Palladian grouping of fountains, pavings, and palazzo became an excellent expression of the preindustrial world, where people looked at things in fixed, primitive, one-point perspective. Symmetry, balance, formality— these were the ordering devices of design. In the city-beautiful era public art was puffed with pomp and plaster. Many examples are still around, singing their stilted old comic-light-opera song. A few have been relocated or revitalized and thereby serve as link between old and new, as in the fountain for the Cincinnati Fountain Square urban renewal project by Archibald Rogers. But many others are lifeless and should be reevaluated.

Whether old and refurbished or constructed anew, the successful public attraction will be the one that involves and stimulates the consumer. To achieve this objective, the designer needs to determine how best to use and intensify the various qualities of water. He can use its many unique properties to do so. Light reflection, for example, can be most distinctive. As water falls in droplets or sheets, it has different degrees of luminosity and brilliance. The effects that can be achieved range from sparkling jewels to shimmering sheets of molten metal.

Daylight penetrating to the paving texture of a shallow container can make water seem transparent and colorless. Or water can be made to look like the blue sky when light is reflected from a deep pool. And at night artificial light, programmed to be variable in color brightness and source, will enable people to experience a water of multiple moods.

Fountain, "Paul Revere" Church, Boston. Public art, dry, "don't touch."

Reston, Virginia.

Another strong quality of water is movement in infinite degree. To pre-determine the activity and intensify the effect can make water fascinating, whether it is still, running, falling, spraying, or jetting high against the sky. Agitation of water will produce endless effects, depending on the method used. Projections rising from a channel can break and make choppy the surface of flowing water. An edge can aerate water falling over it, make it noisy and alive. If serrated, the edge will form water threads; if curled, it will make a sheet flow. Pumps and orifices of various pressures and apertures can make water bubble, foam, spray, or roar in a spectacular jet. In wintry air steamy vapor rising from heated water can add another dimension. With movement comes still another variable quality—sound. "Hsss," "plop plop plop plop," "fwooshhh."

Finally, containers, depending on their shape, size, and elevation, can offer the pedestrian elixir to drink, can encourage the young at heart to splash and wade, can be sculpture whose forms are animated by water.

The designer does not lack for drawing-board options. He can take his pick. But pick he must: the degree to which the public experience of water is to be intensified in each of its aspects—sound, movement, reflection, containers—should be predetermined. First, however, program management requires analysis of the suitability and entertainment value of water to the site, and then a decision on what degree of user involvement is desirable. Then comes the choice of approach and specific means making the experience of water a bigger thing in city dwellers' lives.

THE NEED FOR GREEN

A harsh synthetic environment makes people hunger for softness and living color. The more polluted the urban atmosphere, the more necessary are sweet odors. The more dehumanized the urban machine, the more essential are romantic expressions of nature. Surely the human animal wants contact with growing and ever-changing green things.

This need has been recognized in the past, as demonstrated by the development of greenbelts and park systems. Many Eastern and Midwestern cities not yet totally urbanized are saved from blight by their canopies of trees. And developers and businessmen accept plantings as a tool for dignifying stores, screening parking lots, beautification of gasoline stations, even the cosmetic concealment of parking meters.

Granted the latent demand and consumer acceptance and considering the demonstrated potential, why have not many more extensive and significant installations been created in our cities' shopping plazas, airports, campuses, and other public places?

Several difficulties, natural and man-made, inhibit successful plantings. Perishability of product is obvious. Climate can be severe. Many plant forms and methods of installation are not suitable for the polluted and synthetic urban environment. The average city loses more dead and diseased trees than are planted per year. Tree losses in Buffalo, New York, due to Dutch elm disease exceeded 7,700 for 1968, for a total of more than 50,000 trees since the disease was first spotted in 1951. And traditional budgets and procedures will not make a city green.

Vandalism is another problem. Of course, not all acts destructive to plant life are willful. Playing children can destroy unprotected plants or small trees

Fresno Mall.

without malicious intent. On the other hand, many plantings, formal in their isolation, set-apartness, and perfection, seem to be saying, "Look but don't touch," and like KEEP OFF THE GRASS signs may invite antisocial behavior.

Another problem in the cities may be poor subsurface conditions for trees. Basement vaults under sidewalks require expensive foundations and drainage for root balls. But an even greater problem inhibiting use of plant materials may be the design process itself. The potential of plants as urban furnishings of social utility and value has not been clearly demonstrated in a systematic way.

Greenery Systems Solutions

Even in the design of amenities, goals must be established. Before installing a planter or a fountain, it is necessary to ask what its symbiotic value is. That is, what will the proposed element of decoration do to enhance the environment as a whole? Greenery has traditionally been used to reduce urban harshness or to serve as a focal display point. What other, interrelated tasks can be accomplished?

Greenery can be additionally used as visual linkage to unify a varied streetscape. It can act as buffer between traffic and people. It can guide and control pedestrians. It can moderate the effects of climate and light. Depending on choice of plant form, it can reinforce the desired imagery of the community or area.

Atlanta, Georgia Plaza project. Multiuse art form: pool, pedestrian bridge, bandstand.

Mass-produced multipurpose planter bench.

All of these uses imply quantity consumption and therefore cost reduction through mass production and installation. But unless plant-life survivability is improved, natural landscape elements will still be increasingly replaced by simulated shapes in synthetic materials. Examples now abound of concrete parasols and aluminum space frames replacing live trees. Next will come artificial shrubs and trees. Some improvement in survivability can be expected through development and use of more hardy strains. But more progress will be made in lengthening the life-replacement cycle and reducing costs through design of more protective installations.

In order for greenery to compete with other media for providing pleasure or imagery, considerable improvement is required in choice of containers and method of siting. Placement may be obtrusive or awkward in the pedestrian area. When specially designed for a specific site, planters tend to be overdesigned, too decorative, monumental—a distraction rather than an enhancing use of plant life. Greater concern must be demonstrated for relationship of container to contents. Available off-the-shelf containers may be incompatible with the proposed plant life. Planter and plant must go together, in size, shape, color, and material. For greater plant variety, a family

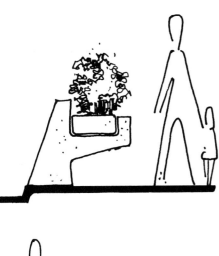

or hierarchy of planter sizes may be necessary. A container of well-chosen height, up-down, in-out, with respect to plane of floor, may make plantings more effective visually. Perhaps planters that would be not merely root containers, but capsules for all parts of the plant, leaves and all, might be introduced.

A system of self-regulating containers, although initially relatively costly, can substantially reduce vandalism, perishability, and maintenance labor. Ideally, such containers would be constructed with integral sprinkler heads and controls, would be connected to the city water supply and self-irrigating, would be climate-controlled by means of heating elements, and would be more completely enclosed for protection from wind, disease, pollution, and vandals.

To give the consumer the enjoyment of a sense of participation or involvement with plant life is obviously a more complex task than to secure his visual gratification. In the past the city provided the arboretum or zoological gardens as not only a showcase for exhibition of exotic plants but also a romantic place to be, to wander, to seek personal release and self-refreshment. Today the need is to take the gardens to the people and to make their overall effect more important than the individual objects in them. To achieve the latter, various components such as ground cover, shrubs, and trees should be assembled to interest and entice by overall sight, smell, sound, and movement. Experimentation might develop novel combinations of organic components or organic and synthetic components which would achieve previously unobtainable effects. Programmed movement and/or nighttime activation of light and shadow on leaf forms might give parks and gardens an altogether new appeal. Street lighting and supplementary light sources should be utilized that enhance plant colors. Variable controls and display trimmings would permit special effects and seasonal variation. These techniques will help make greenery competitive with other psyche-pleasing design options.

People no longer carry their own lanterns at night. The city provides light. People have been deprived of plant life. The city must give it back. When designers and industry develop more viable products and installation techniques, the city will be able to meet this responsibility.

HULLABALOO

The sight of Old Glory rippling in the breeze is great, but hearing seventy-six trombones with it is better. In marking a celebration or symbolizing a theme, there is no such thing as too much of a good thing. One must not only wave the flag but also shoot the works.

The techniques of pageantry have always produced favorable responses

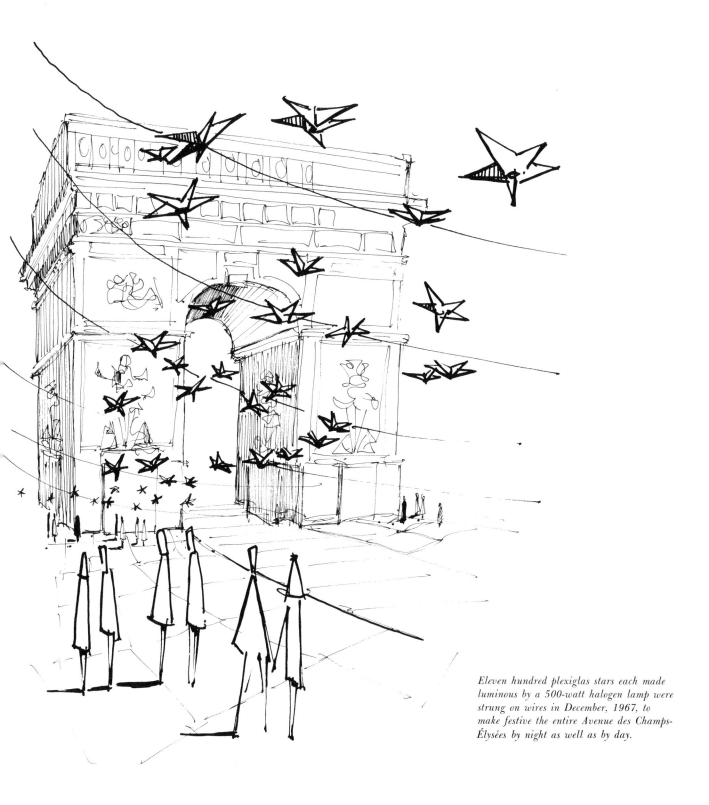

Eleven hundred plexiglas stars each made luminous by a 500-watt halogen lamp were strung on wires in December, 1967, to make festive the entire Avenue des Champs-Élysées by night as well as by day.

Church Street project. At Christmastime hoops of red bulbs are placed around the white lights, creating a halo effect.

in observers. Medieval social and political structure owed much of its glamour and acceptance to the proud symbols and brightly colored devices of heraldry on pennants and knightly trappings. When the town replaced the castle as the center of the civilized world, it also faced the need to provide crowd-pleasing excitement and set out to do so. In America innumerable spectacular attractions evolved in support of community events: bonfires and bands for political rallies, booths and bunting for fund-raising picnics, fireworks for the Fourth of July.

Pageantry, from the setting out of flags for parades to the use of festoons on streetlights to add yuletide spirit to the shopping season, has always been important in marking Main Street, but today the need for bright display in the public space is greater than ever. More restrictive codes and regulations regiment the appearance of the public right-of-way. The monotony and confusion of most downtown American streets call for the imaginative resources of the urban designer—it is no longer enough for him just to provide flagpole sockets along the curb.

A number of old techniques as well as contemporary devices can be used. Air is free, and the wind provides movement. Banners—big, bold, and ebullient—are always acceptable. New excitement can be provided by more experimental and aerodynamic shapes. Semirigid and new lightweight materials can be flown in eye-catching ways. Wild graphics and color patterns will prove again that the bizarre does things for any bazaar.

Light remains a largely unexploited resource. By day, sunlight can be caught, multiplied, patterned, directed by reflective, spinning disks or mirrors. By night, the common crisscross of searchlights on clouds can be supplemented at ground level by spectacular strobe or high-intensity light sources. Multicolored light sources with flashers can be used in clusters or in intriguing arrangements for pinpoint patterns. Banks of bulbs can be programmed to tell time, animate cartoons, or flash graphic images in coordination with time-phased prerecorded avant-garde music.

Whatever the medium, spontaneity and excitement are the qualities the designer needs to capture in the program. If he succeeds there, he will fulfill his opportunity to provide crowd-pleasing hullabaloo.

Chapter Twelve

Put It All Together

In many creative efforts, book as well as song, the reprise restates the theme. Hopefully, it lingers as something to hum as well as to haunt. So it is with this chapter.

By now we know that the city is an artifact. The city is a product conceived, built, and inhabited by man.

By now we know this product is not only obsolete and ugly but also static and unresponsive to the changing needs of man. For the city is not yet a people-serving system. It is an accretion built by a fragmented industry. Unified direction has not been provided by the fragmented local bureaucracy. The urban environment has not been improved because the consumer too is fragmented. There has been an absence of a vocal consumer group with authority, responsibility, resources, and decision-making capability.

By now we know cosmetic tranquilizers do not cure more deep-rooted and harmful problem areas. Use of a better typeface for a "CURB YOUR DOG" sign indicates awareness, but. . . . But elimination of visual pollution requires far more sweeping solutions in all sectors of communications and control.

By now the essence of the systems approach—the interrelationship of site planning with public improvements and physical facilities whether for health and security or fun and games—is clear.

By now we know that whereas in 1900 only 30 percent of the people lived in urban areas, it won't be long before 80 percent of a vastly larger population will be living on only 1½ percent of the land. This is the challenge of our age.

Priorities are constantly being reordered. The national housing goal has been stated to be "a decent home and a suitable living environment for every American family." Although financial institutions and developers have been cautious in accepting site planning and design innovations, HUD has publicized well-designed federal-supported projects through the Design Awards Program and provided incentives to enable other cities to do the same. It remains to sing out loud and clear the new opportunities to plan, design, and furnish more liveable cities, to put it all together, to use subsoil rights as well as air rights, to achieve a cubic city.

With volume production of housing and environment as a national goal, with industrialization as the process, new techniques can be applied which spin off many benefits. With quantity output as a goal, more sophisticated design tooling and production techniques can produce lower unit costs. Cost reduction permits, for the first time in this country, the deflation of the popular notion that in the public environment good design costs more. Quantity can make quality available to everybody.

Additionally, the opportunity exists to create a new idiom, new forms of visual community identity and environmental imagery of appeal to the people. Although it is in the American tradition to pass over the old and to seek the new, the consumer has not been given a marketplace choice—until now.

ILLUSTRATION ON PPS. 234, 235:
Market Street East, Philadelphia. Multi-level, five-block transportation-shopping spine.

THE IMAGE IS MORE THAN SKIN DEEP

Up and Over/Down and Under

Economic forces increasingly act to optimize use of diminishing and expensive urban space. Rising costs have become the impetus for more technically innovative and comprehensive urban design solutions. Older precedents exist. Grand Central City in New York has been described by Douglas Haskell as "the world's finest interlocked multilevel demonstration of the futurist city." That complex was designed almost seventy-five years ago. It has been an obvious functional success engendering considerable consumer affection and loyalty in the process.

Surprisingly few functionally significant Center City complexes have been built since. Noteworthy among those few which successfully interrelate transportation, shopping, office, or hotel use are Midtown Plaza in Rochester, N. Y., Place Ville Marie, Montreal, Charles Center, Baltimore, and Capital Centre in St. Paul. More recent are The World Trade Center sponsored by the New York Port Authority and Market Street East, nurtured for some years by the Philadelphia City Planning Commission and Redevelopment Authority.

Each of these innovative complexes required design of subsystems such as floor, lighting, and signage of quality comparable with the basic structure. As stated in the 1966 Market Street East report by Skidmore, Owings & Merrill, "The plan demands physical integration of all parts of the Transportation–Commerce Center and shared structures and mechanical systems." In these comprehensively designed environments the failure of any subsystem is immediately self-evident and destructive to total system performance.

The commercial success of these and similar projects should redirect urban professionals and developers from a preoccupation with *appearance* to the exploitation of the potential of *design*. Such a fundamental omni-

Multiuse, multilevel World Trade Center, New York.

SUBWAYS

CONSULATES & TRADE CENTERS

PRODUCT DISPLAY

MECHANICAL EQUIPMENT

TRUCK DOCKS

OFFICES

PATH TERMINAL

PARKING

STORAGE

TOWER LOBBY ELEVATORS

CUSTOMS BLDG.

NORTH TOWER BUILDING

NORTHEAST PLAZA BUILDING

WEST ST.

CHURCH ST.

P L A Z A   L E V E L

CONCOURSE   (CONNECTS ALL BLDGS.)

PATH TERMINAL

directional point of view must surely require a high order of technical innovation in physical site improvements as well as buildings. Constraints, such as traditional curb lines and subsurface systems (water, electricity, communications), which presently control the location of visible elements above, must be reevaluated. The place to begin is the site—not only terrain but utilities.

Utilities and service systems have been buried beneath the public street bit by bit until the earth has been repetitively punctured for pipes, conduit, and ductwork in an ever-changing mix of unknown composition and location. Manhole covers, meter and valve-box plates scattered all over the street and sidewalk signal the jumbled array below. Underneath the intersection of Fourth and Vine in downtown Cincinnati, for example, are: a 6-inch water main; an abandoned 6-inch gas main now carrying electric cable; a 10-inch gas main; the Cincinnati Gas and Electric Company's electric circuits for traffic lights, fire and burglar alarms; streetlights; telephone-company circuits; a Western Union electrical duct; Postal Telegraph lines; and underneath it all a great big sewer—*each in its separate trench.*

Typically, the arteriosclerosis of this aged plumbing barely keeping the city alive is ignored until the city street must be laid open. Then the numerous surgical scars crossing paving and walk remind us of the need for frequent repairs to the vital circulatory, communications, and waste systems pulsing below. Crowded, overloaded, and expensive to maintain, these networks cannot accept new functions. They are inadequate to meet rising standards of performance and the needs of a growing population.

Consider for example the need to separate storm and sanitary sewers which in combined form now serve 36 million people. It is well known that the overflow of storm water flushes raw sewage down the sewers and pollutes our streams. But the cost of correction has been estimated in a survey for the Interior Department at 48 billion dollars.

Despite such needs public spaces and streets are designed today by the same procedure used a hundred years ago. All too frequently the designer decides upon *visible* spatial relationships first and only then turns the work over to an engineer who tells him it can't be built that way because of the high capital cost of twisting and straining pipes and ducts into that configuration. Dozens of urban design studies with extensive street changes have remained paper studies because of the failure to tie above grade work to subsurface conditions, to design and fund adequately the *invisible* improvements as well as appearance factors. Rather that a constraint, the design of subsurface features can become an expressive element in the total design. Designs should be created that enable industry to produce with available technology standard units which, assembled in required combinations, can be the spatial utility lattice that supports our environmental needs. Thus an

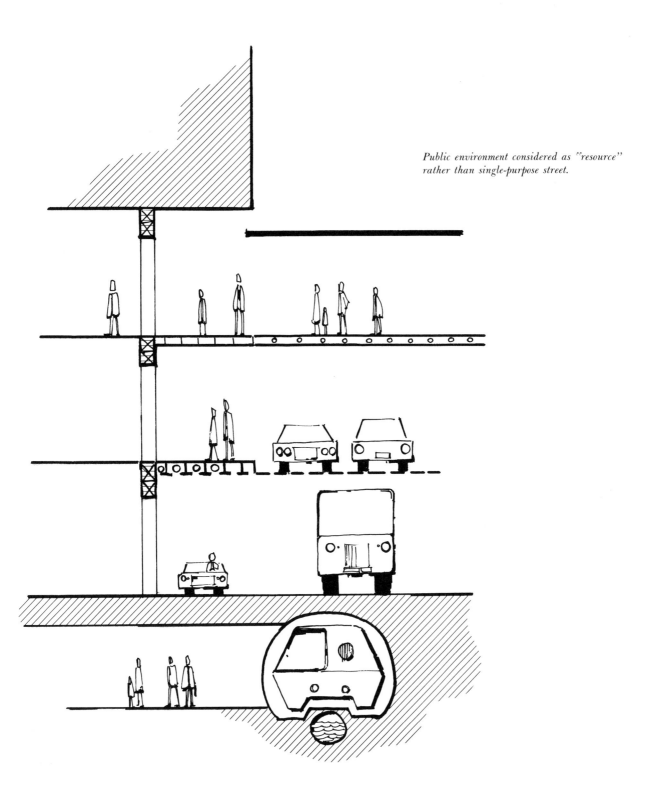

Public environment considered as "resource" rather than single-purpose street.

industrialized approach leads to availability of appropriate elements to assemble utility networks which more economically and cooperatively locate and service the desired urban furnishings.

It is then possible to realign electrical distribution lines together in compact harness much like in the synthetic environment of aircraft. Many pipes and conduit can be grouped into a common duct or chase with a continuous access cover. In certain areas, such as Downtown, where access needs for service or change are greater a service tunnel would be useful. The tunnel should be large enough to accommodate service crews in special vehicles. Some such tunnels are in partial use in a few cities and even campuses. There they permit rapid access to and frequent change and expansion of services. They simplify inspection, maintenance, and repair of utilities without above-grade disturbance. The technology for the service vehicles exists as evidenced by the many special-purpose motorized units used by maintenance and ground crews at airports.

Downtown, if the below-grade utility raceway, the at-grade sidewalk, and the above-grade pedestrian pathway were all aligned as one total space, their separation could be achieved by horizontal partitions of new materials and function. New techniques could give these thin membranes other task potential and spin-off benefits. The separator or floor could contain mechanisms which move people automatically. Access, whether to service mechanical walkways above or utilities below, could be constant and linear, rather than through holes dug in the street. With a constant raceway, the plug-in and connection of street furnishings above to the service systems below is made less costly. Like gas lanterns, manhole covers would become decorative collectors' items, symbols of a bygone Victorian technology.

The potential can be even greater and more quickly achieved in new towns and housing developments of large scale or density.

The seventies will be noted for the significant flow reversal outward from the central business district to the surrounding neighborhoods. This residential environment represents a far greater marketing area and therefore increased potential to industry and the developer. It is assuredly of greater social importance to the individual resident. The residential neighborhood is being developed increasingly by technically innovative design and management techniques spurred by HUD incentives and the housing demand.

Although most shelter designs have followed conventional layout and appearance, economies of scale have shown that industrialized housing may offer more product for less money quicker. As shelter becomes industrialized the product will be further adapted to serial production which will promote greater change of form and materials.

Whatever form shelter takes, vertical stack or horizontal plug-in, the environmental designer must be the catalyst relating the technological prod-

Floating City. Industrialized shelter, stores, schools, roads, and utilities are fitted into a frame and replaced when obsolete.

uct to user needs. More advanced facilities underground are required to support the social environment of greater dimensions above.

Maintaining Environmental Integrity

When the change from product attitude to process behavior takes place, software such as programming instructions become necessary. Implementation of the urban systems design through the procurement, installation, operation, and maintenance phases of hardware will require development of standard procedures for the guidance of the various city agencies and departments. Availability of a *Street Furnishings Manual* is essential to the maintenance of a flexible system with many variables and the assurance of design and management control of quality standards as the system changes.

Many precedents exist in other disciplines and applications. The preparation of systems and components manuals is commonplace in the military–industrial establishment. And the integrity of corporate identity (communications) programs is protected by *Graphic Standards* manuals prepared by designers which show not only minutae such as typeface style and size but approved manner of utilization in all media including vehicles, buildings, and spaces.

Transportation systems too have their *Standards,* one of the foremost being that for the British Railway System prepared by Jock Kinneir.

Unique or complex environmental systems, such as fairs, required manuals prepared by designers for the use of construction and maintenance personnel.

Innovative site developments always required definitive construction documents. As the procedure becomes industrialized, the supporting software necessarily changes and assumes additional functions. Drawings and specifications in new formats describe interrelationships, specify performance standards for future construction or procurement purposes, predetermine possible configurations and combinations for most effective installation, advise optimum operation procedures, and mandate maintenance and change procedures which best protect the system integrity.

Thus we see that the systems view encompasses all phases of urban planning, design, installation, and operation. Nor should feedback from the consumer, as discussed earlier, be omitted. Such an approach can offer the consumer a more comprehensively furnished urban environment for his use and enjoyment.

Design the process, not the product.

Bibliography

There are many hard-cover works on urban design in general, but few that consider the street and its urban furnishings in depth. Only those standard works with some direct utility have been noted. The bulk of useful information appears in periodicals or project documents of limited circulation. When available, these have been noted. Each item is listed only once, under the chapter in which it was first used as a primary or secondary source.

GENERAL

Alexander, Christopher: "Relational Complexes in Architecture," *Architectural Record,* New York, September, 1966.

Chermayeff, Serge, and Christopher Alexander: *Community and Privacy,* Doubleday & Company, Inc., Garden City, N.Y., 1963.

Cullen, Gordon: *Townscape,* The Architectural Press, London, 1961.

Duke University, Caudill Rowlett Scott, Hewes Holz, and Willard: *Computer Aided Campus Planning,* interim report, Educational Facilities Laboratories, Inc., New York, 1967.

Ewald, William R., Jr.: *Environment for Man; Environment and Change; Environment and Policy, The Next Fifty Years* (3 vols.) Indiana University Press, Bloomington, 1968.

Goodman, William, and Eric Freund (eds.): *Principles and Practice of Urban Planning,* 4th ed., International City Managers' Association, Washington, D.C., 1969.

Malt, Harold Lewis: *Proceedings of the White House Conference on Natural Beauty,* Government Printing Office, Washington, D.C., 1966.

———: *Site Products,* interim report, State University Construction Fund, Albany, N.Y., 1966.

Nairn, Ian: *The American Landscape: A Critical View,* Random House, Inc., New York, 1965.

SCSD: The Project and the Schools, Educational Facilities Laboratories, Inc., New York, 1967.

Chapter 1   Our Hand-me-down Street Furniture

Bacon, Edmund N.: *Design of Cities,* The Viking Press, Inc., New York, 1967.

Giedion, Sigfried: *Space, Time and Architecture,* 4th ed., Harvard University Press, Cambridge, Mass., 1963.

Spreiregen, Paul D.: *Urban Design,* McGraw-Hill Book Company, New York, 1965.

Wolf, Peter M.: *Eugène Hénard and the Beginning of Urbanism in Paris* 1900–1914, International Federation for Housing and Planning, The Hague, 1969.

Chapter 2   The Problem

Doxiadis, C. A.: *Urban Renewal and the Future of the American City,* Public Administration Service, Chicago, 1966.

Pushkarev, Boris, Christopher Tunnard, and Ralph Warburton: *Man-made America: Chaos or Control?* Yale University Press, New Haven, Conn., 1963.

Starr, Roger: *The Living End,* Coward-McCann, Inc., New York, 1966.

Wolf, Von Eckardt: *A Place to Live: The Crisis of the Cities,* Delacorte Press, New York, 1967.

Chapter 3   The Systems Approach

Alexander, Christopher: *Notes on the Synthesis of Form,* Harvard University Press, Cambridge, Mass., 1964.

Campbell, Robert D., and Hugh L. LeBlank: *An Information System for Urban Planning,* U.S. Government Printing Office, Washington, D.C., 1967.

Eberhard, John P.: "Technology for the City," *International Science and Technology,* September, 1966, pp. 18–29.

Emerging Techniques of Architectural Practice, The American Institute of Architects, Washington, D.C., 1966.

Hall, Arthur D.: *Systems Engineering,* D. Van Nostrand Company, Inc., Princeton, N.J., 1962.

Metropolitan Data Center Project, Department of Housing and Urban Development, Housing and Home Finance Agency, Washington, D.C., 1966.

"Performance Design," *Progressive Architecture,* August, 1967, pp. 104–153.

State University Construction Fund: *Guide for Campus Planning,* Albany, N.Y., 1965.

Van Foerster, Heinz: "Logical Structure of Environment and Its Internal Representation," International Design Conference, Aspen, Colo., 1962.

Chapter 4   Consumer Is King

Alexander, Christopher: *The City as a Mechanism for Sustaining Human Contact,* Institute of Urban and Regional Development, University of California Press, Berkeley, 1966.

Gagne, Robert M., and Arthur W. Melton: *Psychological Principles in System Development,* Holt, Rinehart and Winston, Inc., New York, 1963.

Gibson, James J.: *The Perception of the Visual World,* Houghton Mifflin Company, Boston, 1950.

Hall, Edward T.: *The Hidden Dimension,* Doubleday & Company, Inc., Garden City, N.Y., 1966.

————: *The Silent Language,* Fawcett Publications, Inc., Greenwich, Conn., 1968.

Luckiesh, M.: *Visual Illusions,* 2d ed., Dover Publications, Inc., New York, 1965.

Chapter 5   Shaping the City Floor

Burrage, Robert H., and Edward G. Mogren: *Parking,* The Eno Foundation for Highway Traffic Control, Saugatuck, Conn., 1957.

Gruen, Victor, and Larry Smith: *Shopping Towns U.S.A.,* Reinhold Publishing Corporation, New York, 1960.

Halprin, Lawrence: *New York, New York,* Department of Housing and Urban Development, Washington, D.C., 1968.

Highway Research Board: *Automobile Parking: Selected References, 1962–1964,* Washington, D.C., 1965.

Lewis, David: *The Pedestrian in the City,* D. Van Nostrand Co., Inc., Princeton, N.J., 1966.

Lynch, Kevin: *The Image of the City,* The M.I.T. Press, Cambridge, Mass., 1966.

Metrotran-2000: A study of Future Concepts in Metropolitan Transportation for the Year 2000, Cornell Aeronautical Laboratory, Inc., Buffalo, N.Y., 1967.

Rudofsky, Bernard: *Streets for People: A Primer for Americans,* Doubleday & Company, Inc., Garden City, N.Y., 1969.

Chapter 6   Posts and Post Mortem

American Association of State Highway Officials: *Specifications for Design and Construction of Structural Supports for Highway Signs,* Bureau of Public Roads, Washington, D.C., 1968.

Chapter 7   City Lights

American Standards Association: *ASA Practice for Roadway Lighting,* IES, New York, 1964.

Cassel, Arno, and Douglas Medville: *Economic Study of Roadway Lighting,* Highway Research Board, Washington, D.C., 1966.

Lam, William M. C.: "The Lighting of Cities," *Architectural Record,* June, 1965, pp. 210–214.

Larson, Leslie: *Lighting and Its Design,* New York Whitney Library, New York, 1964.

Middleton, Michael, and Peter Whitworth: *Suiting the Setting,* conference paper no. 4, Brighton, 1965, The Association of Public Lighting Engineers, London, 1965.

Waldram, J. M.: "Surface, Seeing and Driving: Some Recent Studies," *Light and Lighting,* vol. 53, no. 11, p. 305, November, 1960.

Westermann, H. O.: "Planning Public Lighting for X-Town," *International Lighting Review,* vol. 17, no. 3, 1966.

Chapter 8   People on Wheels

AASHO: *Manual on Uniform Traffic Control Devices for Streets and Highways,* Bureau of Public Roads, Washington, D.C., 1961.

Froshaug, Anthony: "Road-side Traffic Signs," *Design,* no. 178, pp. 36–50, Oct. 1963.

Council on Uniform Traffic Control Devices for Canada: *Manual of Uniform Traffic Control Devices for Canada,* 2d ed., Canadian Good Roads Association, Ottawa, 1966.
Hanson, Daniel, et al.: "Curb Parking Sign Study," *Highway Research Record,* no. 151, pp. 18–40.
Kinneir, Jock: "Designing a System for Britain's Road Signs," *Design,* 221, May, 1967.
Ministry of Transport: *Traffic in Towns,* H. M. Stationery Office, London, 1963.
Ministry of Transport: *Traffic Signs for Motorways: Final Report of the Advisory Committee,* H. M. Stationery Office, London, 1962.
————: *Traffic Signs Manual,* H. M. Stationery Office, London, 1965.
———: *Traffic Signs Manual,* H. M. Stationary Office, London, 1965.
Ritter, Paul: *Planning for Man and Motor,* The Macmillan Company, New York, 1964.

Chapter 9 When People Need to Know or Talk

"Alarm Signal Systems," in *National Fire Codes,* National Fire Protection Association, Boston, 1965, vol. 7, secs. 71, 74.
Brinkley, John: *Lettering Today,* Reinhold Publishing Corporation, New York, 1965.
Krampen, Martin: "Signs and Symbols in Graphic Communication," *Design Quarterly,* Walker Art Center, Minneapolis, 1962.
Malt, Harold Lewis: "Systems for Civic Furnishings," *Industrial Design,* October, 1966, pp. 50–52.
Oster, G., and Y. Nishijima: "Moiré Patterns," *Scientific American,* 208, pp. 54–63, May, 1963.
Sutton, James: *Signs in Action,* Studio Vista, Ltd., London, 1965.

Chapter 10 Good Housekeeping and the Good Life

"Fire Hydrants," in *National Fire Codes,* National Fire Protection Association, Boston, 1965, vol. 7, sec. 29C.

Chapter 11 Pride, Pomp, and Planter

Halprin, Lawrence: *Cities,* Reinhold Publishing Corporation, New York, 1964.
Redstone, Louis G.: *Art in Architecture,* McGraw-Hill Book Company, New York, 1968.
Simonds, John Ormsbee: *Landscape Architecture: The Shaping of Man's Natural Environment,* F. W. Dodge Company, a Division of McGraw-Hill, Inc., New York, 1961.

Illustration Credits

All drawings and photographs not otherwise credited are the work of the author. Position on page is indicated as follows: T = top, B = bottom, L = left, R = right, M = middle.

Index

Date Due